PRENTICE HALL

TOOLS FOR A CHANGING WORLD

Chapter 2
Support File

Functions and
Their Graphs

PRENTICE HALL
Upper Saddle River, New Jersey
Needham Heights, Massachusetts

ISBN: 0-13-43324-1

Printed in the United States of America
1 2 3 4 5 6 7 8   02 01 00 99 98 97

Editorial, design, and production services: Publishers Resource Group, Inc.

PRENTICE HALL
Simon & Schuster Education Group
A VIACOM COMPANY

Chapter 2

Functions and Their Graphs

Alternative Activity: Teacher's Notes **for 2-1**

Analyzing Data Using Scatter Plots

TYPE OF ACTIVITY: Technology (Computers)

CONCEPTS: This Alternative Activity covers the same concepts as Example 1 Relating to the Real World on page 60 of the student text. It uses exactly the same data to show students how to make a scatter plot using a spreadsheet program on a computer.

MATERIALS: Computer, spreadsheet software, Alternative Activity 2-1 student worksheet

---

FACILITATING THE ACTIVITY

In this activity, students use a spreadsheet software program on a computer to draw the graph on page 60. Drawing the scatter plot using a computer introduces students to the power of technology. This also enables them to compare the results that they see on the computer screen with the graph in their textbooks.

Using a Spreadsheet to Make a Data Table

Exercise 1

ERROR ALERT! The given table shows four columns. Students may think four columns are necessary, rather than two. Remediation: Have students check the headings above each column for repetitions.

Exercise 2

Explain that cells in a spreadsheet can be used to show the title of the graph and the labels for the columns. Students can choose how many rows they use for this. For example the label "hours watched" can take up either one or two rows.

Exercise 3

If necessary, provide help for students to enter all of the data from the table into the spreadsheet.

Drawing a Scatter Plot Using a Spreadsheet Program

Most spreadsheet programs contain the ability to make charts and graphs from the data in the spreadsheet. Help students find the graphing capability for their software. If you are using Excel, see the instuctions below. After students have completed their scatter plots, have them compare their graph with the graph on page 60 of their textbook. Then they can answer the remaining questions on the Alternative Activity worksheet.

Creating a Scatter Plot Using Excel

The simplest way to create any graph in Excel is to use ChartWizard.

1. In the spreadsheet worksheet, select the data you want to plot, including cells containing any category or series names that you want to use in the chart.

2. To start ChartWizard, click on the ChartWizard button or the On This Sheet command (Insert menu, Chart submenu).

3. Move back to the highlighted data and click on it.

4. Follow the instructions in the ChartWizard for steps 1–5. In step 4, be sure to indicate that column 1 represents the *x* data.

Alternative Activity: Student Worksheet for 2-1

Analyzing Data Using Scatter Plots

USING A SPREADSHEET TO MAKE A DATA TABLE

Look at the **A Test of Television** table. You will use the information from the table to create a data table using the spreadsheet on your computer.

A Test of Television

hours watched	test score	hours watched	test score
0	92	2	80
0	100	2.5	65
0.5	89	2.5	70
1	82	3	68
1	90	3.5	60
1	95	4	65
1.5	85	4.5	55
2	70	5	60

What You'll Learn
Using a spreadsheet to make a scatter plot

What You'll Need
Computer, spreadsheet software

1. How many columns should your spreadsheet table contain?

2. Enter the title and the headings for each column in the first two rows of the table.

3. Fill in the spreadsheet on the computer screen using the data from the table.

Drawing a Scatter Plot Using a Spreadsheet Program

4. Use the information that you have entered into the spreadsheet to create a scatter plot on your computer screen.

Use the scatter plot to answer these questions.

5. Two students in the sample watched 2.5 h of television. What does the graph tell you about the students' test scores?

6. **a.** One of the students, Travis, scored 60 on the test. How many hours of television did he watch?
   b. How can you tell by looking at the scatter plot?

7. Based on the information in the graph, do you think there is any relationship between the number of hours of television watched and the test score?

Alternative Activity: Teacher's Notes **for 2-3**

Linking Graphs to Tables

TYPE OF ACTIVITY: Work Together

CONCEPTS: This Alternative Activity covers the concept of choosing an appropriate scale for the graph in the Example Relating to the Real World on page 70 of the student text. It uses exactly the same data as on page 70 to show students the effect of various scales and intervals.

MATERIALS: Graph paper and pencil, Alternative Activity 2-3 student worksheet

---

FACILITATING THE ACTIVITY

In this activity, students work in groups of four. Each member of the group draws a graph of the data in the chart, but each uses a different set of scales and intervals. Students then compare their graphs and discuss how different scales and intervals affect the usefulness of the graph.

Choosing a Scale and Interval

Before students begin to make their graphs, work through the process of selecting an appropriate scale and interval based on a table of data. Stress that it is important to choose an appropriate scale so the data is easy to graph and understand. Use the data in the table "How Altitude Affects Temperature" on the student worksheet.

Ask:

- *Would 0 to 10,000 be an appropriate scale for altitude? Why or why not?* **No; the maximum altitude of 10,761 would not appear on the graph.**

- *Would a scale of -50 to 20 be appropriate for the temperature?* **yes**

- *If the scale for temperature were -50 to 20, would intervals of 3 be appropriate? Why or why not?* **No; zero would not appear since 50 is not a multiple of 3. Also -50, -47, -44 would be strange markings to appear.**

- *What would be appropriate intervals for -50 to 20?* **Answers may vary. Sample: 5 or 10**

Drawing the Graph

Exercise 1

Remind students that the x-values correspond to the altitudes. You might also suggest that they label the x-axis in thousands of meters to make the labels simpler.

ERROR ALERT: Students working on Graph D may not know how to label 500 m if the x-axis is to be labeled in thousands of meters. **Remediation:** Explain that 500 m is half (or 0.5) of 1000 m. Have them label the axis 0.5, 1, 1.5, 2, and so on.

Exercise 3

Discuss problems with Graphs A, B, and C. Students may notice that in Graph A the first three points were difficult to plot accurately. Students should see that Graph B uses a scale that is much larger than necessary. Much of the graph is not used for showing the data in the table. The intervals in Graph C are too large making it very difficult to plot accurately on this graph.

Exercise 4

If intervals are too large, it is difficult to graph the data accurately.

Exercise 7

Have volunteers share their questions with the class.

Alternative Activity: Student Worksheet for 2-3

Linking Graphs to Tables

Work in groups of four. Look at the data in the table.

How Altitude Affects Temperature

altitude (m)	temperature (degrees C)
0	13.0
144	12.0
794	11.4
1501	11.4
3100	5.6
5781	−9.7
7461	−22.5
9511	−36.3
10,761	−44.9

What You'll Learn
Choosing appropriate scales and intervals for graphing data

What You'll Need
Graph paper, pencil

1. Four sets of scales and intervals are given (Graphs A, B, C, and D). Have each member of your group graph the data using a different set of scales and intervals.

   Graph A: *x*-values: Use a scale from 0 to 12,000 and label intervals of 1000.
   y-values: Use a scale of −50 to 20 and label intervals of 10.

   Graph B: *x*-values: Use a scale from 0 to 20,000 and label intervals of 1000.
   y-values: Use a scale of −80 to 50 and label intervals of 10.

   Graph C: *x*-values: Use a scale from 0 to 12,000 and label intervals of 2000.
   y-values: Use a scale of −60 to 20 and label intervals of 20.

   Graph D: *x*-values: Use a scale from 0 to 12,000 and label intervals of 500.
   y-values: Use a scale of −50 to 20 and label intervals of 10.

2. After you finish drawing your graph, find the other students in your room with the same set of scales and intervals. Compare the graph you drew to theirs.

3. Return to your original group and compare the graph you drew to the graphs of the other members in your group. Which graph (A, B, C, or D) makes the information easiest to use? Why?

4. Which variable is the dependent variable, the independent variable? Explain.

5. Describe what happens to the temperature as the altitude increases.

6. Write a question that might be of interest to a meteorologist and can be answered using the table or graph. Answer the question you write.

Alternative Activity: Teacher's Notes for 2-7

Families of Functions

TYPE OF ACTIVITY: Non-technological approach

CONCEPTS: This Alternative Activity covers the same concepts as Example 2 on page 91 of the student text. It demonstrates an alternative method for correlating graphs with their functions.

MATERIALS: Graph paper and pencil, Alternative Activity 2-7 student worksheet

---

FACILITATING THE ACTIVITY

In this activity, students become familiar with the concept of identifying what function family (linear, quadratic, or absolute value) a graph belongs to based on its shape. Also, students learn how to predict the shape of a graph based on the given function.

Identifying the Family of an Equation

Before beginning this activity, review how to identify a linear function, a quadratic function, and an absolute value function by looking at an equation. (This material was presented in Example 1 on page 91 of the student text.)

Ask:
- *What is the highest possible power of* x *in a linear function?* **1**
- *What is the highest possible power of* x *in a quadratic function?* **2**
- *How can you identify an absolute value function?* **It contains an absolute value expression.**

Have students decide to which family of functions each of these equations belongs.
- $y = 3x + 5$ **linear functions**
- $y = 4x^2 + 5x + 4$ **quadratic functions**
- $y = |x - 9|$ **absolute value functions**

Identifying the Family of a Graph

VISUAL LEARNING This activity encourages students to learn using their visual skills. To help students remember that the graph of a linear function (a function in which the highest possible power of x is 1) is a line, it is suggested that students think about x to the first power as x^1, where the 1 is the symbol for a line. To help students remember that the graph of a quadratic function (a function in which the highest power of x is 2, that is x squared) is shaped like a U, it is suggested that students visualize the word *sq**U**ared* with a large **U** in it. To help students remember that a function containing an absolute value expression is shaped like a V, it is suggested that students picture the expression absolute **V***alue* with a large **V**.

Be sure students understand that the graphs may point either up or down.

Matching Functions with their Graphs

Exercise 3

ERROR ALERT! Sometimes when students are making a graph from a table of values, they may sketch the shape of a quadratic equation in the shape of a V, or sketch the shape of an absolute value equation in the shape of a U. **Remediation:** Have students use the visual clues of x *sq**U**ared* and absolute **V***alue* introduced in this activity.

Students should check their graphs in Exercise 3 with the descriptions of the graphs they made in Exercise 2.

Alternative Activity: Student Worksheet **for 2-7**

Families of Functions

What You'll Learn	**What You'll Need**
Matching graphs and functions; matching functions and graphs	Graph paper and pencil

IDENTIFYING THE FAMILY OF A GRAPH

Linear Functions

$y = 2x - 1$

The highest possible power of x is 1.

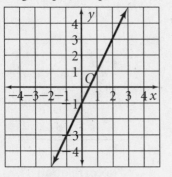

The graph forms a straight line.

Think: x^1 or $x^{\mid}$

Quadratic Functions

$y = 3x^2 - x + 1$

The highest power of x is 2.

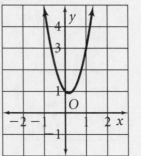

The graph has a U-shaped curve that opens up or down.

Think: x sq**U**ared

Absolute Value Functions

$y = |x - 2|$

There is an absolute value symbol around a variable expression.

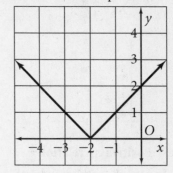

The graph forms a "V" that opens up or down.

Think: Absolute Value

1. To what family of functions does each graph belong?

   a.

   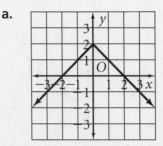

   b.

   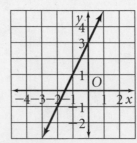

   c.

   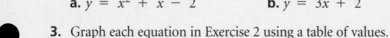

MATCHING FUNCTIONS WITH THEIR GRAPHS

2. To what family of functions does each equation belong? Describe the shape of each graph.

   a. $y = x^2 + x - 2$ **b.** $y = 3x + 2$ **c** $y = |x| - 6$

3. Graph each equation in Exercise 2 using a table of values.

Reteaching 2-1

OBJECTIVE: Analyzing trends in scatter plots   **MATERIALS:** Toothpicks

You can use scatter plots to investigate trends between two sets of data. The trends below show positive, negative, and no correlation. To determine the trend, lay a toothpick on the graph so there are as many points above the line as below the line. If the toothpick goes up from left to right, the graph shows a positive correlation. If the toothpick goes down from left to right, it shows a negative correlation. If the toothpick cannot be placed so that it is close to most points, the data shows no correlation.

Example

Analyze the trend.

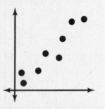

Positive correlation

In general, both sets of data increase together.

Negative Correlation

In general, one set of data decreases as the other set increases.

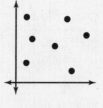

No correlation

Sometimes data sets are not related.

Activity

Use a toothpick to find if there is a positive correlation, negative correlation, or no correlation between the two data sets in each scatter plot.

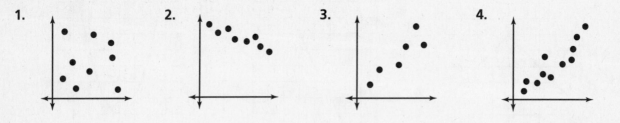

Reteaching 2-2

OBJECTIVE: Interpreting and sketching graphs from stories	**MATERIALS:** None

When you draw a graph without actual data, the graph is called a sketch. A sketch gives you an idea of what the graph will look like. Use the description and the sketch to answer the questions.

Example

Kira rides her bike to the park to meet a friend. When she arrives at the park, Kira and her friend sit on the bench and talk for a while. Kira then rides her bike home at a slower pace.

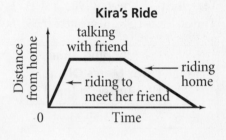

Kira's Ride

1. What does the vertical scale show? It shows distance from home.

2. What does the horizontal scale show? It shows time.

3. Why is the section of the graph showing Kira riding to meet her friend steeper than the section of the graph showing her ride home? Kira was riding faster.

4. Why is the section of the graph flat when Kira is talking to her friend? Kira's distance from home is not changing, but time is still passing.

Activity

To take photographs of the area where you live for a school project, you ride your bike to the top of Lookout Knoll. The road leading to the top is steep. When you arrive at the top, you rest and take some photographs. On the way back down the same road, you stop to take photographs from another location.

1. Draw a sketch of the trip comparing the distance you traveled to time. Label the sections.

2. Which parts of the graph represent your taking photographs? Explain.

3. Which part of the graph is steeper, your ride to the top of Lookout Knoll or your ride down? Explain.

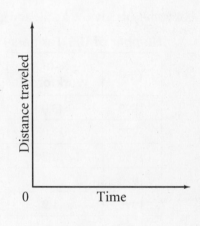

Reteaching 2-3

OBJECTIVE: Choosing a scale and graphing data in tables	**MATERIALS:** Graph paper

Example

Graph the data in the table on a coordinate plane.

To draw a graph, first identify the least and greatest values for each set of data.

Year: least–76, greatest–92
Times: least–1:56:26, greatest–1:59:76

Then, determine a scale that includes these values and can be easily read and interpreted.

Year: 76–92, 4-yr intervals
Times: 1.9–20 min, .05 intervals

Year	Winning Times for Men's Olympic Butterfly (min)
1976	1:59.23
1980	1:59.76
1984	1:57.04
1988	1:56.94
1992	1:56.26

Source: *USA Today*

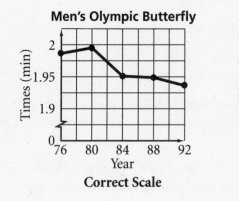

Correct Scale

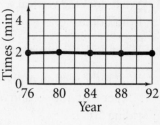

Incorrect Scale

Activity

For each table, choose a scale and graph the data.

1. Number of U.S. Farmers

Year	% of workforce
1890	43.0
1920	27.0
1950	12.2
1970	4.6
1995	1.9

Source: *USA Today*

2. Daily Energy Demand (Avg = 100)

Date of consumption	Avg. daily demand
Jan 1	134
Jan 16	144
Jan 30	137
Feb 15	114
Feb 28	95
March 15	82
March 30	66
April 15	58
April 25	55
April 30	56

Source: *USA Today*

3. Difference in Men's and Women's Running Times

Year	Time Difference
1995	15 min, 13 s
1990	17 min, 5 s
1985	20 min, 1 s
1980	22 min, 17 s
1975	32 min, 31 s
1972	54 min, 13 s

Source: *USA Today*

Reteaching 2-4

OBJECTIVE: Evaluating functions   **MATERIALS:** Number cube

A function rule is an equation that describes a function. If you know the input values, you can use a function rule to find the output values.

$$y = 2x + 5$$

output value   input value

Example

a. Roll a number cube and record the results in the Input Value column of the table. In this example, the first two rolls are 3 and 5.

b. Substitute each Input Value into the function rule to find the Output Value. In this example, the Output Values are 11 and 15.

	Roll (Input Value)	Substitute $y = 2x + 5$	Result (Output Value)
Roll 1	3	$y = 2(3) + 5$	11
Roll 2	5	$y = 2(5) + 5$	15

Activity

Follow steps (**a**) and (**b**) above to evaluate the function.

	Roll (Input Value)	Substitute $y = 4x - 2$	Result (Output Value)
1.			
2.			
3.			
4.			
5.			

Additional Exercises

Evaluate each function rule.

6. $y = -3x + 6$ for $x = 3$ **7.** $y = -5x + 5$ for $x = -2$ **8.** $y = -x$ for $x = -4$

Reteaching 2-5

OBJECTIVE: Writing rules for functions from tables and words	MATERIALS: None

You can write a rule for a function by analyzing a table of values. Look for a pattern in the data table. For each row, ask yourself, "What can I do to the first number to get the second number?" Write the patterns. Circle the pattern that works for all of the data in the table. This is the rule for the function.

Example

x	f(x)	
1	3	← (Add 2) or multiply by 3.
2	4	← (Add 2) or multiply by 2.
3	5	← (Add 2.)

The function rule must be $f(x)$ equals x plus 2. The statement can be written as $f(x) = x + 2$.

Activity

Analyze each table and then write the function rule.

1.

x	f(x)
0	0
1	3
2	6
3	9

2.

x	f(x)
0	−1
1	0
2	1
3	2

3.

x	f(x)
0	0
−1	1
3	9
5	25

Additional Exercises

Write a function rule for each situation. Use letters other than x to represent the variable.

4. The length of a box is two more than four times the width.

5. The width of a sheet of plywood is one-half the length.

Reteaching 2-6

· ·

OBJECTIVE: Graphing a function	**MATERIALS:** Graph paper, number cube

You can use a rule to model a function with a table and a graph.

Example

Graph the function $y = 2x + 3$.

Step 1: Roll a number cube to obtain values for x. Write these values in the first column of the table. Make every other value negative.

Step 2: Evaluate the function to find y for each value of x.

x	$y = 2x + 3$	(x, y)
3	$y = 2(3) + 3 = 9$	$(3, 9)$
-2	$y = 2(-2) + 3 = -1$	$(-2, -1)$
5	$y = 2(5) + 3 = 13$	$(5, 13)$
-1	$y = 2(-1) + 3 = 1$	$(-1, 1)$

Step 3: Plot the ordered pairs to graph the data.

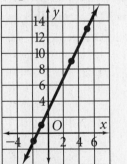

Activity

Model each rule with a table of values and a graph. Roll a number cube to determine the input value for x.

1. $y = 4x + 1$ **2.** $y = x - 2$

3. $y = x + 5$ **4.** $y = 2x^2 + 3$

5. $y = x^2 - 4$ **6.** $y = 3x + 3$

· ·

Reteaching 2-7

• •

OBJECTIVE: Identifying families of functions for equations and graphs   **MATERIALS:** None

You can identify to which family a function belongs based on the shape of its graph.

Example

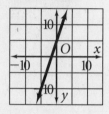

$y = 3x + 5$

The highest power of x is 1; so $y = 3x + 5$ is a **linear function**. Because the graph is a line, one way to remember this is $x^{f\downarrow rst}$.

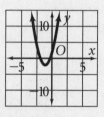

$3x^2 + 7x + 2$

The highest power of x is 2; so $y = 3x^2 + 7x + 2$ is a **quadratic function**. Because this graph is U-shaped, a way to remember this is $x^{sqUared}$.

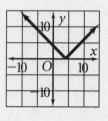

$y = |x - 4|$

The absolute value symbol around the variable tells you that $y = |x - 4|$ is an **absolute value function**. Because the graph forms a "V", remember this as absolute **V**alue.

Activity

To which family of functions does each graph belong? Explain.

1.

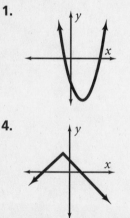

2.

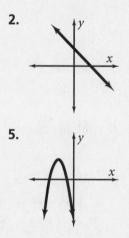

3.

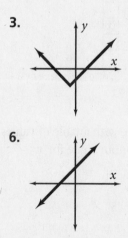

4.

5.

6.

Additional Exercises

To which family of functions does each equation belong? Explain.

7. $y = x^2$

8. $y = |3x + 8|$

9. $y = 9x$

Reteaching 2-8

| **OBJECTIVE:** Finding theoretical probability | **MATERIALS:** None |

The possible results of an experiment are **outcomes**. If you want to find the theoretical probability of a particular event, or a **favorable outcome**, you use this formula.

$$P(\text{event}) = \frac{\text{number of favorable outcomes}}{\text{number of possible outcomes}}$$

Example

Find the theoretical probability of rolling a number cube and having an outcome of either 2 or 4.

$$P(2 \text{ or } 4) = \frac{\text{number of favorable outcomes}}{\text{number of possible outcomes}}$$

$$= \frac{2 \text{ (number of times 2 or 4 are on number cube)}}{6 \text{ (total possible numbers on number cube)}}$$

$$= \frac{1}{3}$$

Activity

You are fishing in a pond stocked with fish. Use the data table at the right to determine the theoretical probability for each favorable outcome. Find each probability.

1. $P(\text{sunfish})$

2. $P(\text{smallmouth bass})$

3. $P(\text{largemouth bass})$

4. $P(\text{sunfish or crappie})$

Sunfish	90
Crappie	33
Smallmouth bass	15
Largemouth bass	12
Total	150

Additional Exercises

Find each probability using the data table in the Activity.

5. $P(\text{catfish})$

6. $P(\text{not a sunfish})$

7. $P(\text{not a crappie or a sunfish})$

Practice 2-1
Example Exercises

Example 1

Use the data in each table to draw a scatter plot.

1.

Minutes Studied	Test Score	Minutes Studied	Test Score
0	60	30	80
0	75	30	90
15	65	45	90
15	70	45	95
15	75	45	100

2.

Cost Ticket	Number Sold	Cost of Ticket	Number Sold
$2.50	100	$3.00	86
$2.50	95	$3.25	84
$2.50	92	$3.25	80
$2.75	96	$3.25	78
$2.75	94	$3.50	80

Example 2

Is there a *positive correlation*, a *negative correlation*, or *no correlation* between the two data sets in each scatter plot?

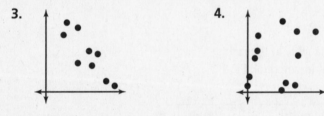

3.   4.   5.

Use the scatter plot below for Exercises 6–9.

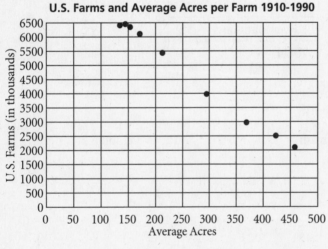

U.S. Farms and Average Acres per Farm 1910-1990

Source: *The Universal Almanac*

6. Sketch a trend line on the graph.

7. Is there a *positive correlation*, a *negative correlation*, or *no correlation* between the average acres and the number of farms?

8. As the average acres per farm increases what happens to the number of farms?

9. **Predict** the number of U.S. farms when the average acres value is 500.

Practice 2-1

· ·

Mixed Exercises

Use the data in each table to draw a scatter plot.

1. **Height and Hourly Pay of Ten People**

Height (inches)	Hourly Pay	Height (inches)	Hourly Pay
62	$6.00	72	$8.00
65	$8.50	72	$6.00
68	$6.50	73	$7.50
70	$6.00	74	$6.25
70	$7.50	74	$8.00

2. **Speed of Winds in Some U.S. Cities**

Station	Average Speed (mi/h)	Highest Speed (mi/h)
Atlanta, GA	9.1	60
Casper, WY	12.9	81
Dallas, TX	10.7	73
Mobile, AL	9.0	63
St. Louis, MO	9.7	60

Source: National Climatic Data Center

3. In Exercise 1, is there a *positive correlation*, a *negative correlation*, or *no correlation* between the height and the hourly pay?

4. In Exercise 2, is there a *positive correlation*, a *negative correlation*, or *no correlation* between average wind speed and highest wind speed?

Would you expect a *positive correlation*, a *negative correlation*, or *no correlation* between the two data sets? Why?

5. a person's age vs. the number of pets

6. number of times you brush your teeth vs. number of cavities

7. number of days a year it rains vs. number of umbrellas sold

Is there a *positive correlation*, a *negative correlation*, or *no correlation* between the two data sets in each scatter plot?

8.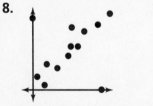

9.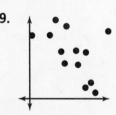

10.

Use the data in the table below for Exercises 11–13.

Years Employed	3	3	4	5	5	7	9	10	12
Salary ($)	24,000	25,000	26,000	28,000	29,000	30,000	33,000	34,000	40,000

11. Draw a scatter plot. **12.** What type of correlation is there between the two data sets?

13. Predict the salary of an employee who has worked 6 yr.

· ·

Practice 2-2

• •

Example Exercises

Example 1

The graph shows the relationship between time and total distance traveled by a teacher riding a bus.

1. What does the flat part of the graph represent?

2. The first section of the graph is steeper than the last section. Was the bus traveling faster in the first part of the trip or the last?

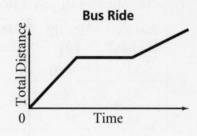

The graph shows the speed a student traveled on the way to school.

3. What do the flat parts of the graph represent?

4. Circle the sections of the graph that show speed decreasing.

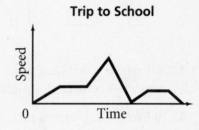

Example 2

Sketch a graph to describe the following. Explain the activity in each section of the graph.

5. the height an airplane is above the ground flying from Dallas, TX to Atlanta, GA.

6. the speed of a person driving to the store and having to stop at two stoplights

Example 3

Classify the data as *continuous or discrete.* Explain your reasoning.

7. the floors an elevator stops on in a high-rise office building

8. the air temperature over a 24-h period

9. the class attendance each day for a week

10. the number of people eating in a restaurant each day for a week

11. the number of cars in a parking lot each day for a week

Practice 2-2

. . . .

Mixed Exercises

Classify the data as *continuous* or *discrete*. Explain your reasoning.

1. your body temperature over a 24-h period

2. daily movie attendance for a week

3. wind speed over a 24-h period

The graph shows the relationship between time and distance from home.

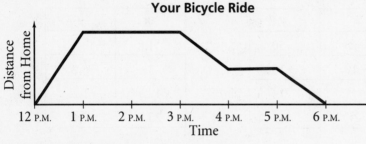

Your Bicycle Ride

4. What do the flat parts of the graph represent?

5. What do the sections from 3 P.M. to 4 P.M. and from 5 P.M. to 6 P.M. represent?

6. What does the section from 12 P.M. to 1 P.M. represent?

Sketch a graph to describe the following. Explain the activity in each section of the graph.

7. your elevation above sea level as you hike in the mountains

8. your speed as you travel from home to school

Classify the data as *continuous or discrete*. Explain your reasoning.

9. the number of books checked out of the library each day for a month

10. the height above the ground as an airplane travels from New York to Los Angeles

The graph shows the relationship between time and speed for an airplane.

Speed vs. Time

11. Circle the sections of the graph that show the speed increasing.

12. Circle the section of the graph that shows the plane not moving.

13. Circle the section of the graph that shows the plane moving at a constant speed.

Practice 2-3

Example Exercises

Example

Identify the independent and dependent variables.

1. total cost of gas, number of gallons of gas

2. perimeter of square, length of a side

3. total cost of item, change from ten-dollar bill

4. total calories, number of slices of bread

Choose scales and intervals that you could use to graph each table.

5.

x	y
−5	10
2	20
6	43
13	52

6.

x	y
−28	−50
−19	−10
−11	0
2	20

7.

x	y
1.0	−13.9
3.6	−6.7
12.9	1.2
25.7	2.4

Graph the data in each table.

8.

x	y
0	0
1	1
2	4
4	16
6	36

9.

x	y
−2	−8
−1	−6
2	0
5	6
7	10

10.

x	y
−2.6	2.76
−1.2	−2.56
0	−4
1.5	−1.75
3.5	8.25

11. The table to the right shows the effect of a 10 mi/h wind on the wind chill temperature.

   a. What are the independent and dependent variables?

   b. Graph the data.

   c. What will the wind chill be when the temperature is 15°F?

Temperature	Wind Chill
30°F	16°F
20°F	3°F
10°F	−9°F
0°F	−22°F
−10°F	−34°F

Source: National Weather Service

12. The table shows the interest earned on a savings account of $5000 at 5% interest compounded annually.

Length of Savings (yr)	1	2	4	7
Interest Earned ($)	250	512.50	1077.53	2035.50

   a. From the table, what can you say about the relationship between the length of savings and the interest earned?

   b. Identify the independent and dependent variables.

   c. Graph the data.

Practice 2-3

Mixed Exercises

Graph the data in each table.

1.

x	y
−4	18
−2	6
−1	3
2	6
3	11

2.

x	y
−3	−5
−1	−1
0	1
1	3
4	7

3.

x	y
−2.3	6.3
−1.7	5.1
0.5	0.7
1.2	−0.7
4.8	−7.9

Identify the independent and dependent variables.

4. cost of pencils, number of pencils

5. cost of item, change from twenty-dollar bill

6. speed of car, distanced travel

7. amount of sales tax, cost of items

Choose a scale that you could use to graph each table.

8.

x	y
−5	10
2	−6
6	−15
13	−23

9.

x	y
−18	−30
−13	−10
−5	25
2	75

10.

x	y
1.0	12.5
3.6	10.5
12.9	7.5
25.7	3.6

11. The table shows the cost for purchasing square yards of carpet.

Carpet (yd²)	10	15	20	30
Total Cost ($)	199.50	299.25	399.00	590.50

   a. From the table, what can you say about the relationship between the amount of carpet and the total cost?

   b. Identify the independent and dependent variables.

   c. Graph the data.

12. The table shows the cost to rent a car for one day at $20 plus mileage.

Miles Driven (mi)	50	100	150	200
Total Cost ($)	27.50	35.00	42.50	50.00

   a. Identify the independent and dependent variables.

   b. Graph the data.

   c. Use the graph to approximate the cost of renting the car and driving 120 mi.

   d. From the table, what can you say about the relationship between miles driven and total cost to rent the car?

Practice 2-4

•••

Example Exercises

Example 1

Determine if each relation is a function.

1.

x	y
10	−5
15	1
27	6
29	7
36	8

2.

x	y
2	2
6	4
4	8
0	0
2	6

3.

x	y
−6	6
−3	6
4	6
8	6
9	6

4.

x	y
−6	2
−4	2
−2	4
−3	4
−4	4

Example 2

Evaluate each function rule.

5. $y = 5x - 2$ for $x = 3$

6. $y = x - 1$ for $x = -2$

7. $y = 2x - 13$ for $x = 8$

8. $y = 6(x - 6)$ for $x = 7$

9. $y = \frac{1}{2}x + 8$ for $x = 6$

10. $y = \frac{2}{3}x - 2$ for $x = 6$

11. $y = 6x - 4$ for $x = 1.5$

12. $y = \frac{3}{4}x$ for $x = -2$

13. $y = 3x + 2$ for $x = 5$

14. $y = 2(x + 9)$ for $x = -4$

15. $y = 2x^2 - 1$ for $x = 4$

16. $y = 3x^2 + 5$ for $x = 5$

Example 3

Find the range of each function when the domain is {−3, 0, 3}.

17. $t = 2s$

18. $m = 1.5n$

19. $y = \frac{1}{3}x$

20. $p = 4q - 6$

21. $m = 2.5n - 1.5$

22. $a = \frac{b + 15}{3}$

23. $y = x^2$

24. $y = \frac{1}{9}x^2$

Find the range of each function when the domain is {2, 4, 6}.

25. $f = 2g$

26. $s = 3t + 1$

27. $z = y^2$

28. $d = 4(8 - c)$

29. $a = \frac{3}{2}(b + 2)$

30. $y = \frac{12 - x}{2}$

31. $y = x^2 - 5$

32. $b = \frac{12}{c}$

33. $p = \frac{3(6 - q)}{2}$

© Prentice-Hall, Inc.

Practice 2-4

• •

Mixed Exercises

Evaluate each function rule.

1. $y = 3x + 4$ for $x = 8$

2. $a = b - 6$ for $b = -2$

3. $m = n^2 + 8$ for $n = 5$

4. $s = -2t^2 + 3$ for $t = 4$

5. $p = 3q - 6$ for $q = 9$

6. $e = 15 - f$ for $f = 3$

Determine if each relation is a function.

7.

x	y
−2	2
0	4
2	6
3	6

8.

x	y
−5	3
2	−2
7	1
2	3

9.

x	y
−3	3
−1	5
0	2
−3	4

Find the range of each function when the domain is {−2, 0, 2}.

10. $j = 3k - 5$

11. $y = 3x^2 - 2x$

12. $d = -4.5e + 2.6$

13. $m = \frac{3}{2}n - 8$

Evaluate each function rule.

14. $y = 2x - \frac{1}{2}$ for $x = \frac{3}{4}$

15. $a = 3(8 + b)$ for $b = -3$

16. $d = 4.2e$ for $e = 3$

17. $g = -3(19 - h)$ for $h = 15$

18. $s = 2(t + 7)$ for $t = -5$

19. $m = 4n + 3$ for $n = 2.5$

Find the range of each function when the domain is {−1, 3, 5}.

20. $y = 3x + 2$

21. $a = 2(8 - b)$

22. $m = 25n$

23. $p = 2(q - 1)$

Evaluate each function rule.

24. $m = \frac{3}{4}(1 - n)$ for $n = \frac{1}{2}$

25. $y = \frac{2}{3}x$ for $x = \frac{9}{10}$

26. $a = b^2 + 2.2$ for $b = 3$

27. $c = 5(4d - 8)$ for $d = 2$

28. $a = \frac{2}{3}\left(\frac{3}{4} + b\right)$ for $b = \frac{1}{4}$

29. $y = x^2 - \frac{1}{4}$ for $x = \frac{1}{2}$

Find the range of each function when the domain is {−2, 2, 4}.

30. $y = \frac{3(6 - x)}{2}$

31. $a = \frac{20}{b}$

32. $m = \frac{1}{2}n + 3$

33. $y = \frac{2.5x}{2}$

Practice 2-5

Example Exercises

Example 1

Write a function rule for each table.

1.

x	f(x)
0	10
1	11
2	12
3	13

2.

x	f(x)
0	0
2	10
4	20
6	30

3.

x	f(x)
0	0
1	1
2	4
3	9

4.

x	f(x)
−4	−1
−2	1
2	5
4	7

5.

x	f(x)
0	0
3	6
6	12
9	18

6.

x	f(x)
−2	0
0	2
2	4
4	6

7.

x	f(x)
1	0
3	2
5	4
7	6

8.

x	f(x)
−3	−9
−1	−3
2	6
5	15

9. Find $f(5)$ for Exercise 1

10. Find $f(8)$ for Exercise 2

11. Find $f(6)$ for Exercise 3

12. Find $f(-1)$ for Exercise 4

13. Find $f(2)$ for Exercise 5

14. Find $f(7)$ for Exercise 6

Example 2

15. A car is 30 times larger than its scale model.

    a. Write a function rule to describe this relationship.

    b. If the model is 6 in. long, how long is the car?

    c. If the model is 2.5 in. wide, how wide is the car?

16. Pencils cost $.20 each.

    a. Write a function rule to calculate the total cost of any number of pencils.

    b. Use your rule to find the total cost of 12 pencils.

Example 3

17. You invest $209 to buy shirts and then sell them for $9.50 each.

    a. Write a function rule to determine your profit.

    b. Use your rule to find your profit after selling 24 shirts.

    c. How many shirts do you need to sell to get back your investment?

18. A car rental agency charges a fee of $25 plus $.20 for each mile driven.

    a. Write a function rule to determine the cost of renting a car.

    b. Use your rule to find the cost of renting a car and driving 150 miles.

© Prentice-Hall, Inc.

Practice 2-5

. . . .

Mixed Exercises

Write a function rule for each table.

1.

x	f(x)
0	3
2	5
4	7
6	9

2.

x	f(x)
0	0
1	3
3	9
5	15

3.

x	f(x)
5	0
10	5
15	10
20	15

4. a. Write a function rule to calculate the cost of buying bananas at $.39 a pound.

   b. How much would it cost to buy 3.5 pounds of bananas?

5. To rent a cabin, a resort charges $50 plus $10 per person.

   a. Write a function rule to calculate the total cost of renting the cabin.

   b. Use your rule to find the total cost for six people to stay in the cabin.

Find $f(2)$ for each function.

6. $f(x) = 6 - x$

7. $f(x) = 6x + 7$

8. $f(x) = x^2 + 5x$

9. $f(x) = -3x^2$

10. $f(x) = 2 + 4x$

11. $f(x) = 9 - x^2$

Write a function rule for each table.

12.

x	f(x)
-4	-2
-2	-1
6	3
8	4

13.

x	f(x)
-3	9
0	0
1	1
5	25

14.

x	f(x)
0	20
2	18
4	16
8	12

Find the range of each function when the domain is {0, 1, 5}.

15. $f(x) = 2x^2 - x$

16. $f(x) = 27 - 3x$

17. $f(x) = -x + 8$

18. Pens are shipped to the office supply store in boxes of 12 each.

   a. Write a function rule to calculate the total number of pens when you know the number of boxes.

   b. Calculate the total number of pens in 16 boxes.

19. a. Write a function rule to determine the change you would get from a twenty-dollar bill when purchasing items that cost $1.25 each.

   b. Calculate the change when five of these items are purchased.

   c. Can you purchase 17 of these items with a twenty-dollar bill?

Practice 2-6

• •

Example Exercises

Example 1

Model each rule with a table of values and a graph.

1. $f(x) = x - 6$ **2.** $f(x) = 15 - x$ **3.** $f(x) = -5x$

4. $f(x) = \frac{1}{2}x + 2$ **5.** $f(x) = -\frac{2}{3}x + 4$ **6.** $f(x) = 5 - 3x$

7. $f(x) = 2x - 3$ **8.** $f(x) = -x - 2$ **9.** $f(x) = 3x - 8$

10. A motel charges $50 per night for a room. The total cost of a stay at the motel is a function of the number of nights stayed.

     a. Use the rule $C(n) = 50n$ to make a table of values and then a graph.

     b. What is the cost to spend 13 nights in the motel?

     c. Should the points on the graph be connected by a line? Explain why or why not.

11. The speed in ft/s that an object falls is a function of time in seconds.

     a. Use the rule $S(t) = 32t$ to make a table of values and then a graph.

     b. What is the speed when the time is 1.5 seconds?

     c. Should the points on the graph be connected by a line? Explain why or why not.

Example 2

Graph each function.

12. $y = x^2$ **13.** $y = 2x^2$ **14.** $f(x) = x^2 - 4$

15. $f(x) = -x^2 + 5$ **16.** $f(x) = x^2 - 1$ **17.** $f(x) = -x^2 + 1$

18. $y = x^2 - 2x + 1$ **19.** $f(x) = -3x^2 + 2x$ **20.** $f(x) = x^2 + 3x - 5$

Example 3

Make a table of values for each graph.

21.
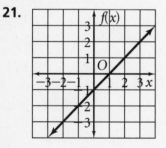

22.
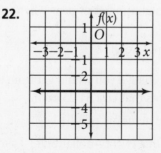

23.
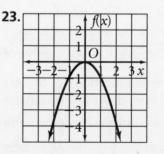

Name _____ Class _____ Date _____

Practice 2-6
• •
Mixed Exercises

Model each rule with a table of values and a graph.

1. $f(x) = x + 1$ **2.** $f(x) = 2x$ **3.** $f(x) = 3x - 2$

4. $f(x) = \frac{3}{2}x - 2$ **5.** $f(x) = \frac{1}{2}x$ **6.** $f(x) = -\frac{2}{3}x + 1$

7. $f(x) = x^2 + 1$ **8.** $f(x) = -x^2 + 2$ **9.** $f(x) = x - 3$

10. Suppose a van gets 22 mi/gal. The distance traveled $D(g)$ is a function of the gallons of gas used.

   a. Use the rule $D(g) = 22g$ to make a table of values and then a graph.

   b. How far did the van travel when it used 10.5 gallons of gas?

   c. Should the points of the graph be connected by a line? Explain.

11. The admission to a fairgrounds is $3.00 per vehicle plus $.50 per passenger. The total admission is a function of the number of passengers.

   a. Use the rule $T(n) = 3 + 0.50n$ to make a table of values and then a graph.

   b. What is the admission for a car with six people in it?

   c. Should the points of the graph be connected by a line? Explain.

Model each rule with a graph.

12. $f(x) = 4x + 2$ **13.** $f(x) = x^2 - 2x + 1$ **14.** $f(x) = -3x + 7$

15. $f(x) = x^2 - 3$ **16.** $f(x) = 8 - \frac{3}{4}x$ **17.** $f(x) = \frac{2}{3}x - 7$

18. $f(x) = -\frac{2}{3}x + 6$ **19.** $f(x) = x^2 - 5$ **20.** $f(x) = -\frac{1}{2}x + 3$

21. $y = 5x - 10$ **22.** $y = 9 - x^2$ **23.** $y = 10 - 3x$

Make a table of values for each graph.

24.
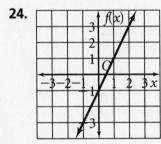

25.
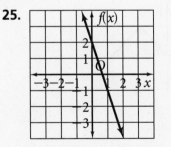

26.
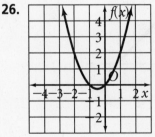

© Prentice-Hall, Inc.

• •
Algebra Chapter 2   The Three Views of a Function   **29**

Practice 2-7

•••

Example Exercises

Example 1

What is the characteristic of the equation for each family of functions?

  1. linear function   **2.** quadratic function   **3.** absolute value function

To what family of functions does each equation belong? Explain why.

  4. $y = 3x + 3$ **5.** $y = -5x$ **6.** $y = x^2$ **7.** $y = |x - 2|$

  8. $y = -\frac{1}{2}x$ **9.** $y = -2x^2 + 8$ **10.** $y = \left|\frac{2}{3}x + 9\right|$ **11.** $y = 2x^2 - 5x + 7$

  12. Create two equations that belong to the linear family of functions.

  13. Explain why the equation $y = x - |-8|$ is not an absolute value function.

Example 2

What is the characteristic of the graph for each family of functions?

  14. linear function   **15.** quadratic function   **16.** absolute value function

To what family of functions does each graph belong? Explain why.

17. 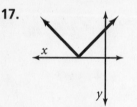   **18.** 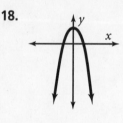   **19.**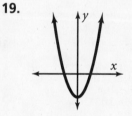

20. 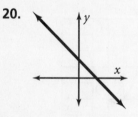   **21.** 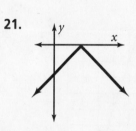   **22.**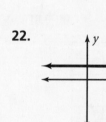

  23. Sketch two graphs that belong to the quadratic family of functions.

Practice 2-7

•••

Mixed Exercises

1. Create three equations that belong to the quadratic family of functions.

2. Create three equations that belong to the absolute value family of functions.

3. Sketch three graphs that belong to the linear family of functions.

To what family of functions does each equation belong? Explain why.

4. $y = 5 - |2x|$

5. $y = 3x^2 - 2$

6. $y = |x - 1|$

7. $y = 10x - 2$

8. $y = |3x| + 2$

9. $y = x^2 + 2x + 5$

10. $y = -\frac{2}{3}x^2 - 5$

11. $y = -3x$

12. $y = 7x + |-3|$

13. $y = 6 - 4x$

14. $y = 3|x + 2|$

15. $y = 4x + x^2$

To what family of functions does each graph belong? Explain why.

16.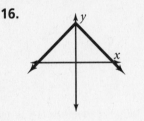

17.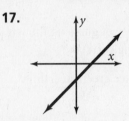

18.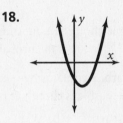

19.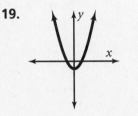

20.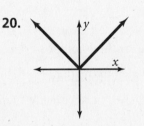

21.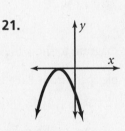

To what family of functions does each equation belong? Explain why.

22. $y = |x - 5|$

23. $y = -\frac{2}{3}x - 5$

24. $y = x + 4$

25. $y = 2 + 3x - x^2$

26. $y = 4x^2 - x$

27. $y = 3 + |2x|$

28. $y = \frac{1}{2}x^2$

29. $y = -5x - 8$

30. $y = 7x - 6$

31. $y = -6|x|$

32. $y = -\frac{8}{9}x - 12$

33. $y = -7x^2 + 7x - 6$

34. $y = 4 + x + x^2$

35. $y = \left|\frac{2}{7}x\right| + 8$

36. $y = -13 - x$

Practice 2-8

••

Example Exercises

Example 1

Teresa has a pile of shoes: a pair of loafers, a pair of tennis shoes, one sandal, and one high-heel. Find each probability for picking one shoe out of the pile.

1. P(getting a sandal)   **2.** P(getting one of a pair)   **3.** P(cowboy boot)

One state is chosen at random from the 50 United States. Find each probability.

4. P(the state is Virginia)   **5.** P(the state begins with A)   **6.** P(the state touches the Pacific Ocean)

Example 2

7. There is a 25% chance of rain tomorrow. What is the probability that it will not rain?

8. On a multiple choice test question, the probability of guessing the wrong response is $\frac{3}{4}$. What is the probability of guessing correctly?

9. A bag of marbles contains two red, four blue, three green, and three yellow. One marble is chosen at random.
   a. What is P(red)?   **b.** What is P(not red)?   **c.** What is P(green or blue)?   **d.** What is P(red or yellow)?

Example 3

10. Draw a tree diagram to show the sample space for three coin tosses.

11. Use the sample space from Exercise 10 to find each probability.
   a. P(exactly 2 tails)   **b.** P(at least 2 heads)   **c.** P(exactly 1 tail)

12. Draw a tree diagram to show the sample space for forming 3-digit numbers with the digits 2, 5 and 7 if the digits may repeat.

13. Use the sample space from Exercise 12 to find each probability.
   a. P(2 appears 3 times)   **b.** P(5 appears at least once)   **c.** P(7 appears exactly once)

14. Use the sample space below for picking two coins out of a bank of one penny, two nickels, two dimes, and two quarters. Find each probability.
   a. P(total is 8¢)
   b. P(total is $\geq$ 15¢)
   c. P(total is 11¢)
   d. P(total is $\leq$ 15¢)

Sample Space for Picking Two Coins			
(5¢, 1¢)	(1¢, 5¢)	(1¢, 10¢)	(1¢, 25¢)
(10¢, 1¢)	(10¢, 5¢)	(5¢, 10¢)	(5¢, 25¢)
(25¢, 1¢)	(25¢, 5¢)	(25¢, 10¢)	(10¢, 25¢)

Practice 2-8

Mixed Exercises

1. One letter is chosen at random from the word *ALGEBRA*.

   a. What is P(the letter is A)? **b.** What is P(letter is a vowel)?

   c. What is P(the letter is A or G)?

2. Patrice has a 40% chance of making a free throw. What is the probability that she will miss the free throw?

3. Jan is writing her name in color. She has a red pen and a blue pen. Jan can use either pen for each letter.

   a. Make a tree diagram to show the sample space. **b.** What is P(the letter n is red)?

   c. What is P(either one or two letters are blue)? **d.** What is P(her entire name is one color)?

4. A box of animal crackers contains five hippos, two lions, three zebras, and four elephants. One animal cracker is chosen at random.

   a. What is P(a hippo)? **b.** What is P(not an elephant)?

   c. What is P(an elephant or a lion)?

5. Anthony is making a collage for his art class by picking shapes randomly. He has five squares, two triangles, two ovals, and four circles.

   a. What is P(circle is chosen first)? **b.** What is P(a square is not chosen first)?

   c. What is P(a triangle or a square is chosen first)?

6. Find each probability for one roll of a number cube.

   a. $P(2)$ **b.** P(even) **c.** P(not 2)

7. Your friend picks a letter of the alphabet. The probability of guessing the correct letter is $\frac{1}{26}$. What is the probability of guessing incorrectly?

8. Two different letter tiles are to be chosen from A, B, C, and D. Find the following probabilities.

   a. Draw a tree diagram to show the sample space.

   b. What is P(A and B are selected)? **c.** What is P(one letter is C)?

   d. What is P(one letter is C and the other letter is A or D)?

9. One digit is chosen at random from the number 18,002,655,328.

   a. What is P(the digit is odd)? **b.** What is P(the digit is greater than 4)?

   c. What is P(the digit is 0, 2, or 5)?

Chapter Project Manager
· ·
Chapter 2 Fast Talker

Getting Started Read about the project on page 57 of your textbook.
To work on the project, you need these materials: a stopwatch or a watch
with a second hand, a poster board, and materials to make graphs that are
accurate and attractive. Keep all of your work for the project in a folder,
including this sheet.

Checklist and Suggestions

❑ Take and record timings. (p. 63)   Organize the data as you collect it.

❑ Draw a scatter plot. (p. 63)   Label the axes carefully.

❑ Record new timings. (p. 72)   You need a group of ten.

❑ Graph new data. (p. 72)   Choose the type of graph best suited to the data.

❑ Calculate values. (p. 83)   Show the steps of your work.

❑ Draw table and graph. (p. 83)   Choose appropriate scales.

❑ Select tongue twister. (p. 94)   See Finishing the Chapter Project (p. 100) for a list
                                                 of resources.

❑ Collect data and graph. (p. 94)   Use the same methods as on page 63.

❑ Write function rule. (p. 94)   Look for a pattern in your data.

Scoring Rubric

3   You complete all work. You make accurate graphs and charts and label
them correctly. Your computations are correct. You write clear
explanations. You write a function rule that corresponds to your data.

2   You make graphs and tables that are mostly accurate and have useful
labels. You do most calculations correctly, with only minor errors. You
write explanations and a function rule that make sense.

1   You make graphs and tables that need additional information. You do
computations and write explanations that are partially correct.

0   You leave out or do not complete important parts.

Your Evaluation of Project Evaluate your work, based on the *Scoring Rubric.*

Teacher's Evaluation of Project

✔ Checkpoint 1

For use after 2-2

1. The table shows height and arm-span measurements for a family of six.

Name	Manuel	Ana	Luís	Rena	Roberto	Felicia
Height (cm)	192	157	178	157	142	119
Arm Span (cm)	191	160	180	156	142	116

    a. Use the data in the table to draw a scatter plot.   **b.** If appropriate, draw a trend line.

    c. Describe the correlation, if any, between height and arm span.

2. **Open-ended** Describe a situation that shows a negative correlation.

3. Which graph could show the total distance you travel as you go from home to a friend's house? Explain why.

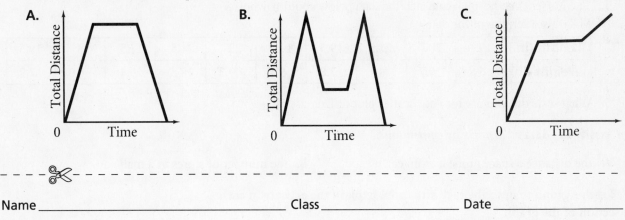

✂ -

✔ Checkpoint 2

For use after 2-5

1. **a.** The table shows the distance that a car travels. Identify the independent and dependent variables.
   b. Graph the data.

2. **Writing** Explain the difference between discrete data and continuous data.

3. **Open-ended** Create a set of ordered pairs that is a relation but not a function.

Number of Hours	Number of Miles
1	55
3	165
5	275
7	385

Write a function rule to describe each statement.

4. the distance you can walk at 3 mi/h

5. the amount of money you make washing cars at $5.50 per car

Find the range of each function when the domain is {−3, −1, 2, 5}.

6. $m = 3(n + 1)$ 7. $b = a^2 − 7$ 8. $s = 2t + 3.5$ 9. $y = 15 − x^2$

Chapter Assessment

Chapter 2

Form A

Is there a *positive correlation*, a *negative correlation*, or *no correlation* between the two data sets in each scatter plot?

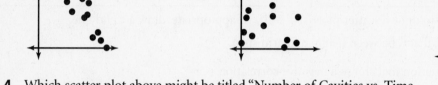

1.   **2.**   **3.**

4. Which scatter plot above might be titled "Number of Cavities vs. Time Spent Brushing Teeth?"

5. The nursery at a hospital collected the data below about newborns. Make a scatter plot of the data.

Length (in.)	19	20	21.5	19.5	19	22	21.5	17.5	18	19.5
Weight (lb)	6.8	9.7	8.1	7.8	8.4	9.3	8.8	5.4	6.3	7.2

6. What scale did you use for your scatter plot of Exercise 5?

Classify the data as *discrete* or *continuous*.

7. the distance a space probe is from earth   **8.** the number of stores in a mall

Sketch a graph to describe each situation. Explain the activity in each section of the graph.

9. the height of an elevator above the ground

10. the speed of a freight train going through the mountains

Determine if each relation is a function.

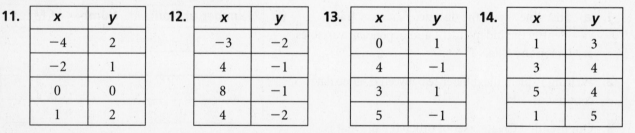

11.

x	y
−4	2
−2	1
0	0
1	2

12.

x	y
−3	−2
4	−1
8	−1
4	−2

13.

x	y
0	1
4	−1
3	1
5	−1

14.

x	y
1	3
3	4
5	4
1	5

Find the range of each function when the domain is {−4, −1, 0, 1.5, 5}.

15. $f(b) = -2b + 6$

16. $f(x) = 3x^2 - 4$

17. $f(g) = g^2 + g$

Chapter Assessment (continued)　　　　　　　Form A

Chapter 2

Write a function rule to describe each statement. Identify the independent and dependent variables.

18. the cost of staying in a motel at $35 per night

19. the amount of money you earn working for $5.50 an hour

20. change from a five-dollar bill when buying apples at $.89 per pound

Model each rule with a table of values and a graph.

21. $f(x) = \frac{3}{2}x + 2$　　　　　**22.** $f(x) = 2x^2 - 3$　　　　　**23.** $f(x) = -2x + 4$

24. Writing Explain when a relation is also a function.

25. Open ended Write a description of a situation that could be modeled by the equation $y = 10 - x$.

26. Which graph is the graph of $y = x^2$?

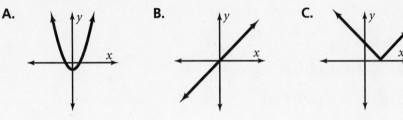 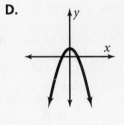

27. A car rental company rents Chevrolets, Fords, Toyotas, and Hondas. The available sizes are compact, midsize, and full-size. All combinations of make and size are equally likely.

    a. Draw a tree diagram and list all the possible combinations of make and size.

    b. Find the probability of randomly selecting a midsize Chevrolet.

28. You roll a number cube and then draw a marble, without looking, from a bag containing one blue, one green, and one yellow marble. What is the probability of getting a 4 on the number cube and then choosing a green marble?

    A. $\frac{1}{6}$　　　　　**B.** $\frac{1}{12}$　　　　　**C.** $\frac{1}{18}$　　　　　**D.** $\frac{1}{3}$

29. Writing Explain how to use the vertical line test to determine if a graph is the graph of a function.

Name _____ Class _____ Date _____

Chapter Assessment
Chapter 2

Form B

Is there a *positive correlation*, a *negative correlation*, or *no correlation* between the two data sets in each scatter plot?

1.    **2.**   **3.**

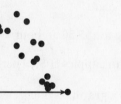

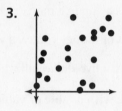

4. Which scatter plot above could be titled "Height of Person vs. Population of Hometown?"

5. What scale would you use to graph the following data?

Waist (in.)	38	32	35	31	29	30	32	36	29	32
Shoe Size	12	10.5	9	8.5	9	12	7	8.5	10	11

6. Draw a scatter plot of the above table.

Classify the data as *discrete* or *continuous*.

7. the points scored in each game during the basketball season

8. the height of the tides measured over a 24-h period

Sketch a graph to describe the situation. Explain the activity in each section of the graph.

9. the temperature in an oven as you start it, bake bread, and turn it off

Determine if each relation is a function.

10.

x	y
−14	12
−8	11
6	13
−14	25

11.

x	y
−13	−8
9	−8
15	7
26	13

12.

x	y
2	7
9	−9
15	8
2	−15

13.

x	y
10	17
25	14
48	17
54	29

Find the range of each function when the domain is {−2, −1, 0, 2.5, 6}.

14. $f(g) = -3g - 7$ **15.** $f(n) = 2n^2 + 4$ **16.** $f(t) = 2.5 + 2t$

Write a function rule to describe each statement. Identify the independent and dependent variables.

17. the distance you walk at 250 ft/min

18. change from a twenty-dollar bill when buying gas at $1.15 per gallon

Chapter Assessment (continued)   Form B

Chapter 2

Model each rule with a table of values and a graph.

19. $f(x) = x^2 - 2$ **20.** $f(x) = 4 - \frac{2}{3}x$ **21.** $f(x) = -x^2 + 2$

22. Writing Explain how relations and functions are the same and how they are different.

23. Open-ended Describe a situation that could be modeled by the equation $y = 2x$.

24. Which graph is the graph of $y = |x|$?

a.
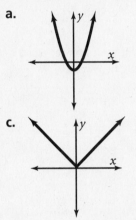

b.

c.

d.

25. A store sells shirts in small, medium, and large. The sleeve length may be short or long. The available colors are white and blue. All combinations of size, sleeve length, and color are equally likely.

    a. Draw a tree diagram and list all possible outcomes of size, sleeve length, and color.

    b. Find the probability of randomly selecting a medium sized blue shirt with short sleeves.

26. A coin is tossed three times. What is the probability of getting at least one tail?

    A. $\frac{3}{8}$ **B.** $\frac{1}{2}$ **C.** $\frac{7}{8}$ **D.** $\frac{3}{4}$

27. State if each graph is the graph of a function or not.

    a.   **b.**   **c.**   **d.**

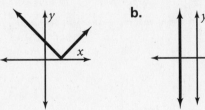
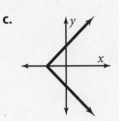
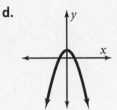

Alternative Assessment

Chapter 2

Give complete answers.

TASK 1

The table below shows the relation between the sizes of typical ready-to-wear boy's clothing and the heights of the boys who wear that size.

Boy's Clothing Sizes

Size	4	5	6	7	8	10	12	14
Height (in.)	39	42	45	49	52	55	59	62

Source: *Sizes*

a. Draw a scatter plot of the data. **b.** What type of correlation exists? **c.** Explain your answer to (**b**).

TASK 2

Invent a story that you can represent with a sketch. (Recall that a graph without actual data is called a sketch.)

a. Write your story using two variables.

b. Explain why the data is discrete or continuous.

c. Draw a sketch to represent your story.

d. Label each section of the sketch.

Alternative Assessment (continued)
Chapter 2

TASK 3

Answer the following questions about functions.

a. Write a paragraph explaining to a friend the meaning of these terms: relation, function, domain, and range.

b. Draw an example of a graph of each of the following functions: linear, quadratic, and absolute value. Then draw two graphs of relations that are not functions. Label each example.

c. Choose one of the function graphs you drew above. Create a table of values. Write a function rule for the graph.

d. Evaluate the function rule $y = 3x^2 + 4$ for $x = -2$. Explain which is the dependent and independent variable. Graph the function.

TASK 4

A car dealer orders these cars: five white, two red, one blue, three black, four green, and three gray. Assume all the cars arrive at the dealer's lot at the same time. The car dealer puts the keys to all the cars in a bowl. The dealer selects keys at random.

a. Find each probability for selecting keys.

P(green) P(red or black)
P(not white) P(blue or white)

b. For which color car is the probability highest?

c. Describe an example of zero probability for this situation.

d. Make a tree diagram to find the sample space for the following situation. The dealer put keys for all the black and gray cars in the bowl. The dealer draws keys for three cars, replacing the key to the bowl each time. What is the probability of selecting keys for exactly two black cars?

Name _____ Class _____ Date _____

Cumulative Review
••
Chapter 2

For Exercises 1–8, select the correct letter.

1. Which line plot shows the following set of data?
   2, 1, 3, 0, 2, 2, 1, 0, 3, 2, 3, 2, 1, 0

   A.
   ```
   x       x
   x  x  x  x
   x  x  x  x
   x  x  x  x
   ─────────────
   0  1  2  3
   ```
   B.
   ```
            x
            x
   x  x  x  x
   x  x  x  x
   x  x  x  x
   ─────────────
   0  1  2  3
   ```
   C.
   ```
            x
   x        x
   x  x  x  x
   x  x  x  x
   x  x  x  x
   ─────────────
   0  1  2  3
   ```
   D.
   ```
               x  x
   x  x  x  x
   x  x  x  x
   x  x  x  x
   ─────────────
   0  1  2  3
   ```

2. What is the value of the expression $6 + 4 \times 2 + 8 \div 4$?

   A. 7   **B.** 25   **C.** 16   **D.** 22

3. Which of the following expressions has a value of 18?

   I. $(4 + 3) \times 2 + 12 \div 3$

   II. $4 + (3 \times 2 + 12) \div 3$

   III. $4 + 3 \times (2 + 12) \div 3$

   A. I only   **B.** II only   **C.** II and III   **D.** I and III

4. Which spreadsheet formula can you use to find the mean of three numbers?

   A. (A1 + B1 + C1)^3   **B.** (A1 + B1 + C1)/3

   C. (A1 + B1 + C1) * 3   **D.** A1 + B1 + C1/3

5. Which matrix is the sum of $\begin{bmatrix} 4 & -4 \\ 3 & -1 \end{bmatrix} + \begin{bmatrix} -2 & 1 \\ -5 & 9 \end{bmatrix}$?

   A. $\begin{bmatrix} 2 & -3 \\ -2 & 8 \end{bmatrix}$
   B. $\begin{bmatrix} 2 & 3 \\ -2 & 8 \end{bmatrix}$
   C. $\begin{bmatrix} -2 & 3 \\ 2 & -8 \end{bmatrix}$
   D. $\begin{bmatrix} 2 & -3 \\ 2 & -8 \end{bmatrix}$

6. Find $f(-4)$ when $f(x) = -x^2 - 2x$.

   A. 24   **B.** 8   **C.** −8   **D.** −24

7. Which of the following relations is not a function?

   A.

x	y
1	2
3	5
4	5
5	5
8	3

   B.

x	y
1	7
3	2
−5	2
4	−3
9	4

   C.

x	y
6	2
−1	6
5	−5
3	9
1	6

   D.

x	y
3	−2
1	5
6	5
8	−1
1	9

© Prentice-Hall, Inc.

Cumulative Review (continued)
Chapter 2

8. Which function is modeled by this table?

x	f(x)
−2	10
0	6
2	2
4	−2

A. $f(x) = -2x + 6$ **B.** $f(x) = x + 6$ **C.** $f(x) = -5x$ **D.** $f(x) = 3x - 4$

For Exercises 9–15, write your answer.

9. Find the range of $f(x) = 2x^2 - 5x$ when the domain is $\{-3, -1, 0, 2\}$.

10. To what family of functions do each of the following belong? Explain your reasoning.

a. $f(x) = 3x + 5$ **b.** $f(x) = x^2 - 6$

c. $f(x) = -4x^2 - 3x$ **d.** $f(x) = |3x - 2|$

11. Writing Explain the difference between discrete data and continuous data.

12. Open-ended Describe a situation that could be modeled by $y = 4x$.

13. Suppose you have a bag containing two red, four blue, three white, and four yellow marbles. One marble is selected at random.

a. Find $P(\text{red})$.   **b.** Find $P(\text{not red})$.   **c.** Find $P(\text{blue or white})$.

14. Suppose you toss two number cubes. Find each probability.

a. $P(\text{sum is 6})$ **b.** $P(\text{sum is at least 10})$ **c.** $P(\text{sum is odd number})$

15. The table shows the distance that an object falls when dropped from an airplane.

Time (s)	1	2	4	7
Distance (m)	4.9	19.6	78.4	240.1

a. Name the independent and dependent variables.

b. Graph the data.

c. How far will the object fall when the time is 5 s?

Standardized Test Practice

Chapter 2

For Exercises 1–10, choose the correct letter.

1. Which of the following data would be classified as discrete?

   A. the number of bananas sold every year

   B. the height of a tree

   C. the barometric pressure

   D. the temperature outdoors between dawn and dusk

2. Which of the following is most likely represented by this graph?

   A. your speed as you walk uphill

   B. the amount of gas in a car gas tank during an afternoon drive

   C. the outdoor temperature during one morning

   D. the weight of a desk

   E. the amount of birthday cake at a party

3. Which of the following is true about a graph of amount of parking fees collected at the beach vs. daily temperature?

   A. The temperature is the dependent variable.

   B. The amount of fees is the independent variable.

   C. The y-values range from 0 m to 100 m.

   D. The independent variable is temperature.

   E. none of the above

4. Which of the following is true?

   A. The graph of $y = x + 8$ is a straight line.

   B. The graph of $y = |x - 10|$ is a U-shaped curve that opens down.

   C. The graph of $y = \frac{1}{2}x^2$ is a straight line.

   D. The graph of $y = x$ is a circle.

   E. none of the above

5. Which one of the following is false?

   A. The dependent variable usually relates to the y-axis.

   B. The value of an independent variable depends on the value of a dependent variable.

   C. The value of a dependent variable depends on the value of an independent variable.

   D. The dependent variable is usually marked on the vertical axis.

   E. none of the above

6. Which of the following is *not* true about the origin?

   A. The x-coordinate is 0.

   B. The graph of $y = x$ passes through it.

   C. It lies in only Quadrant I.

   D. The y-coordinate is 0.

   E. The graph of $y = 0$ passes through it.

7. Compare the quantities in Column A and Column B for the data table.

x	f(x)
−2	3
−1	4
0	5
1	r
2	s

Column A	Column B
r	s

   A. The quantity in Column A is greater.

   B. The quantity in Column B is greater.

   C. The two quantities are equal.

   D. The relationship cannot be determined on the basis of the information supplied.

Standardized Test Practice (continued)

Chapter 2

8. Which of the following is the function rule for this table?

c	$G(c)$
-2	17
-1	5
0	1
1	5
2	17

   A. $G(c) = c + 19$
   B. $G(c) = c^2 + 13$
   C. $G(c) = c^4 + 1$
   D. $G(c) = 3c^2 + 2$
   E. $G(c) = 4c^2 + 1$

9. Compare the quantities in Column A and Column B.

Column A	**Column B**
$3x$	$4x$

   A. The quantity in Column A is greater.
   B. The quantity in Column B is greater.
   C. The two quantities are equal.
   D. The relationship cannot be determined on the basis of the information supplied.

10. Compare the quantities in Column A and Column B.

Column A	**Column B**
P(rolling a 2 on a number cube)	P(rolling a 4 on a number cube)

   A. The quantity in Column A is greater.
   B. The quantity in Column B is greater.
   C. The two quantities are equal.
   D. The relationship cannot be determined on the basis of the information supplied.

For Exercises 11–16, write your answer.

11. Draw a scatter plot for the price of a t-shirt and the number of t-shirts a store might sell each day. Have the x-axis range from $0 to $50 in increments of $5, and the y-axis range from 0 to 100.

12. Draw a speed vs. time graph to show a person walking up and then down a steep hill. Explain the activity in each section of the graph.

13. How can you tell whether a graph is that of a function?

14. Find the range of the function $d = 5 + \frac{1}{2}a$ when the domain is $\{0, 4, 6\}$.

15. **Open-Ended** Draw and label the graphs of a quadratic function and an absolute value function on the same axes.

16. What is the probability that a letter of the alphabet picked at random is a vowel: A, E, I, O, or U?

For Exercises 17–18, mark your answers in the free response grid.

17. Evaluate $y = -x^2 + 7$ for $x = -3$.

18. How many times does the graph of $y = x^2 - 4$ cross the x-axis?

Chapter 2

Bubble Grid Answer Sheet for Standardized Test Practice

1. Ⓐ Ⓑ Ⓒ Ⓓ
2. Ⓐ Ⓑ Ⓒ Ⓓ Ⓔ
3. Ⓐ Ⓑ Ⓒ Ⓓ Ⓔ
4. Ⓐ Ⓑ Ⓒ Ⓓ Ⓔ
5. Ⓐ Ⓑ Ⓒ Ⓓ Ⓔ
6. Ⓐ Ⓑ Ⓒ Ⓓ Ⓔ
7. Ⓐ Ⓑ Ⓒ Ⓓ
8. Ⓐ Ⓑ Ⓒ Ⓓ Ⓔ
9. Ⓐ Ⓑ Ⓒ Ⓓ
10. Ⓐ Ⓑ Ⓒ Ⓓ
11.

16.

17.

18.

12.

13.

14.

15.

Chapter 2 Answers

Alternative Activity 2-1

1. 2 columns

2–3.

A Test of Television

hours watched	test scores
0	92
0	100
0.5	89
1	82
1	90
1	95
1.5	85
2	70
2	80
2.5	65
2.5	70
3	68
3.5	60
4	65
4.5	55
5	60

4.

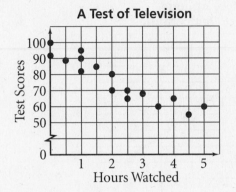

5. One scored 65 and one scored 70.

6a. 3.5 h or 5 h   **6b.** Answers may vary.
Sample: A test score of 60 corresponds to
3.5 h or 5 h on the scatter plot.

7. Answers may vary. Sample: Test scores
seem to decrease as the number of hours of
television increases.

Alternative Activity 2-3

1.

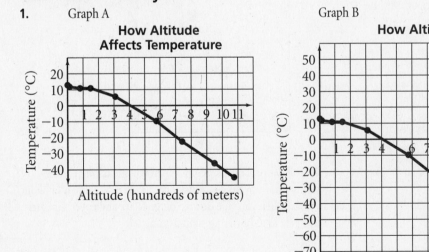

Graph C

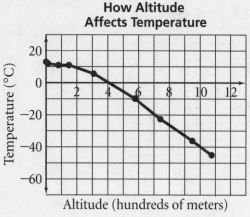

Graph D

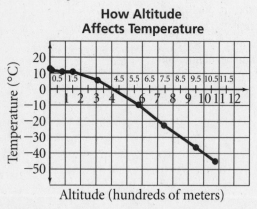

3. Graph D is easiest to read. The scales are appropriate to the data and the intervals are neither too wide nor too narrow.
4. Temperature, altitude: temperature depends on altitude.
5. As altitude increases, temperature decreases.
6. Answers may vary.

Alternative Activity 2-7

1a. absolute value functions **1b.** linear functions
1c. quadratic functions
2a. quadratic functions; a U-shaped curve **2b.** linear functions; a line **2c.** absolute value functions; a V-shape
3a.

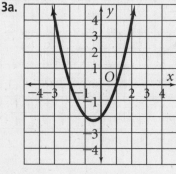

3b.

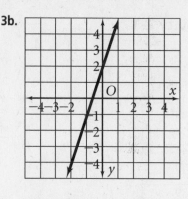

3c.

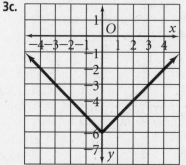

Reteaching 2-1

1. no correlation **2.** negative correlation **3.** positive correlation **4.** positive correlation

Reteaching 2-2

1.

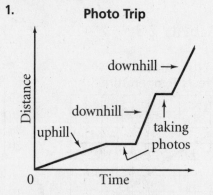

2. The flat part of the graph. When you are taking pictures, you are not traveling any distance. **3.** The ride down Lookout Knoll. When you ride down, you go faster and cover a greater distance in a shorter amount of time.

Chapter 2 Answers (continued)

Reteaching 2-3

1. Answers may vary. Sample:

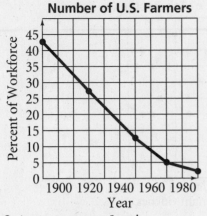

Number of U.S. Farmers

2. Answers may vary. Sample:

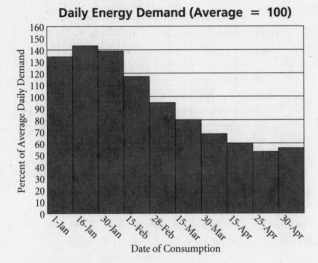

Daily Energy Demand (Average = 100)

3. Answers may vary. Sample:

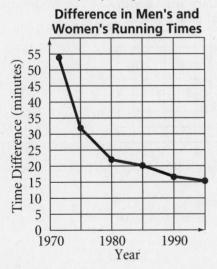

Difference in Men's and Women's Running Times

Reteaching 2-4

1–5. Answers may vary. **6.** -3 **7.** 15 **8.** 4

Reteaching 2-5

1. $f(x) = 3x$ **2.** $f(x) = x - 1$ **3.** $f(x) = x^2$
4. $f(w) = 4w + 2$ **5.** $f(l) = \frac{1}{2}l$

Reteaching 2-6

1–6. Answers may vary. Samples:

1.

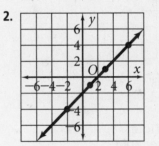

2.

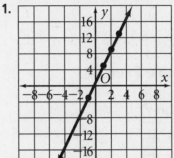

3.

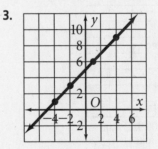

4.

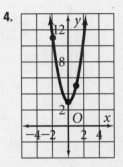

5.

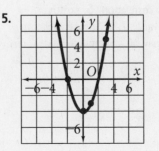

6.

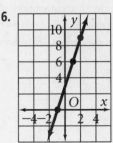

Reteaching 2-7

1. Quadratic function; the graph is U-shaped. **2.** Linear function; the graph is a line. **3.** Absolute value function; the graph forms a V. **4.** Absolute value function; the graph forms a V. **5.** Quadratic function; the graph is U-shaped. **6.** Linear function; the graph is a line. **7.** Quadratic function; x is squared. **8.** Absolute value function; absolute value symbol is around variable expression. **9.** Linear function; x is to the first power.

Reteaching 2-8

1. $\frac{3}{5}$ **2.** $\frac{1}{10}$ **3.** $\frac{2}{25}$ **4.** $\frac{41}{50}$ **5.** 0 **6.** $\frac{2}{5}$ **7.** $\frac{9}{50}$

Practice 2-1: Example Exercises

1.

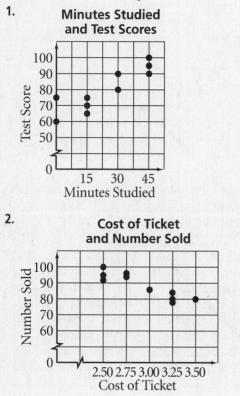

Minutes Studied and Test Scores

2.

Cost of Ticket and Number Sold

3. negative correlation **4.** no correlation **5.** positive correlation **6.** Answers may vary. **7.** negative correlation **8.** It decreases. **9.** Answers may vary. Sample: 1,500,000 farms

Practice 2-1: Mixed Exercises

1.

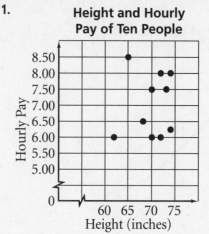

Height and Hourly Pay of Ten People

2.

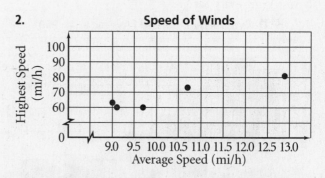

Speed of Winds

3. no correlation **4.** positive correlation **5.** No correlation; a person's age is not related to the number of pets they may have. **6.** Negative correlation; the more times you brush the fewer the cavities you are likely to have. **7.** Positive correlation; the more rainy days the more umbrellas are likely to be sold. **8.** positive correlation **9.** negative correlation **10.** no correlation

11.

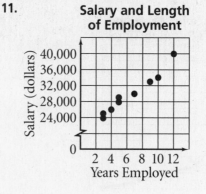

Salary and Length of Employment

12. positive correlation
13. Answers may vary. Sample: $29,000

© Prentice-Hall, Inc.

Chapter 2 Answers (continued)

Practice 2-2: Example Exercises

1. The bus is stopped.   **2.** The bus is traveling faster in the first part.   **3.** The student is traveling at a constant speed.

4.

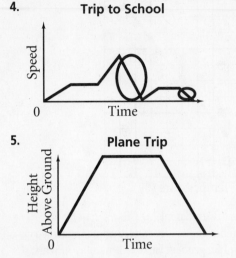

Trip to School

5.

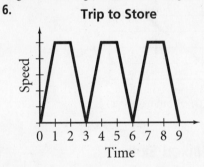

Plane Trip

Answers may vary. Sample: Where the graph is increasing the height above the ground is increasing. Where the graph is flat the height is not changing. Where the graph is decreasing the height above the ground is decreasing.

6.

Trip to Store

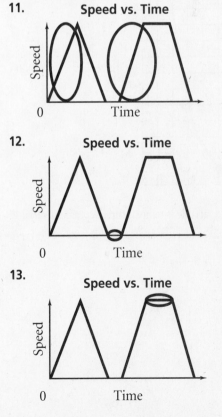

Answers may vary. Sample: In sections 0 to 1, 3 to 4, and 6 to 7, the speed is increasing. In sections 2 to 3, 5 to 6, and 8 to 9, the speed is decreasing. In sections 1 to 2, 4 to 5, and 7 to 8, the speed is constant. At 0, 3, 6, and 9, the car is stopped.
7. Discrete: each floor is distinct.   **8.** Continuous; temperature continues to change during times that it is not measured.
9. Discrete; each day's attendance is distinct.
10. Discrete; each day's count is distinct.
11. Discrete; each day's count is distinct.

Practice 2-2: Mixed Exercises

1. Continuous; body temperature may change even when not being measured.   **2.** Discrete; each day's count is distinct.
3. Continuous; wind speed may be constantly changing.
4. The distance from home is not changing.   **5.** The distance from home decreases.   **6.** The distance from home increases.

7. Answers may vary. Sample: In section 0 to 1, hiker is ascending. In section 1 to 2, the hiker's elevation is constant. In section 2 to 3, the hiker is descending.

Mountain Hike

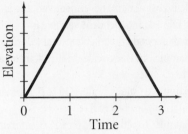

8. Answers may vary. Sample: In section 0 to 1, speed is increasing. In section 1 to 2, speed is constant. In section 2 to 3, speed is decreasing.

Trip to School

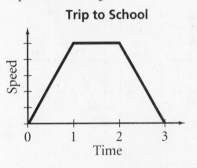

9. Discrete; the number of books is a distinct number.
10. Continuous; the height is always changing.
11.   Speed vs. Time

12.   Speed vs. Time

13.   Speed vs. Time

Chapter 2 Answers (continued)

Practice 2-3: Example Exercises

1. Independent variable is number of gallons of gas; dependent variable is cost of gas.   **2.** Independent variable is length of a side; dependent variable is perimeter of square.

3. Independent variable is cost of item; dependent variable is change from ten-dollar bill.   **4.** Independent variable is number of slices of bread; dependent variable is total calories.

5. Answers may vary. Sample: x-values: scale -6 to 14, interval of 2; y-values: scale 10 to 55, interval of 5

6. Answers may vary. Sample: x-values: scale -30 to 5, interval of 5; y-values: scale -50 to 20, interval of 5

7. Answers may vary. Sample: x-values: scale 0 to 27.5, interval of 2.5; y-values: scale -15 to 2.5, interval of 2.5

8.

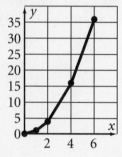

9.

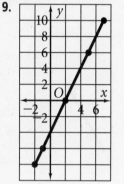

10.

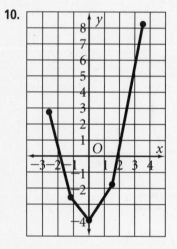

11a. Independent variable is temperature; dependent variable is wind chill.

11b.

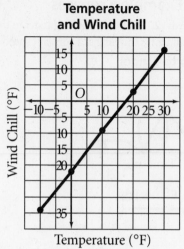

Temperature and Wind Chill

11c. Answers may vary. Sample: $-3°F$
12a. As the number of years increase, the interest earned also increases.   **12b.** Independent variable is number of years; dependent variable is interest earned.
12c.

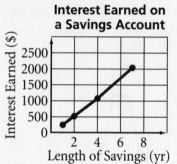

Interest Earned on a Savings Account

Practice 2-3: Mixed Exercises
1.

2.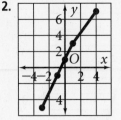

3.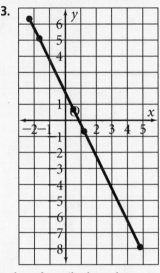

Practice 2-4: Example Exercises
1. yes **2.** no **3.** yes **4.** no **5.** 13 **6.** -3 **7.** 3 **8.** 6
9. 11 **10.** 2 **11.** 5 **12.** $-\frac{3}{2}$ **13.** 17 **14.** 10 **15.** 31
16. 80 **17.** $\{-6, 0, 6\}$ **18.** $\{-4.5, 0, 4.5\}$ **19.** $\{-1, 0, 1\}$
20. $\{-18, -6, 6\}$ **21.** $\{-9, -1.5, 6\}$ **22.** $\{4, 5, 6\}$
23. $\{9, 0, 9\}$ **24.** $\{1, 0, 1\}$ **25.** $\{4, 8, 12\}$ **26.** $\{7, 13, 19\}$
27. $\{4, 16, 36\}$ **28.** $\{24, 16, 8\}$ **29.** $\{6, 9, 12\}$ **30.** $\{5, 4, 3\}$
31. $\{-1, 11, 31\}$ **32.** $\{6, 3, 2\}$ **33.** $\{6, 3, 0\}$

Practice 2-4: Mixed Exercises
1. 28 **2.** -8 **3.** 33 **4.** -29 **5.** 21 **6.** 12 **7.** yes **8.** no
9. no **10.** $\{-11, -5, 1\}$ **11.** $\{16, 0, 8\}$ **12.** $\{11.6, 2.6, -6.4\}$
13. $\{-11, -8, -5\}$ **14.** 1 **15.** 15 **16.** 12.6 **17.** -12
18. 4 **19.** 13 **20.** $\{-1, 11, 17\}$ **21.** $\{18, 10, 6\}$

22. $\{-25, 75, 125\}$ **23.** $\{-4, 4, 8\}$ **24.** $\frac{3}{8}$ **25.** $\frac{3}{5}$ **26.** 11.2

27. 0 **28.** $\frac{2}{3}$ **29.** 0 **30.** $\{12, 6, 3\}$ **31.** $\{-10, 5, 10\}$

32. $\{2, 4, 5\}$ **33.** $\{-2.5, 2.5, 5\}$

Practice 2-5: Example Exercises
1. $f(x) = x + 10$ **2.** $f(x) = 5x$ **3.** $f(x) = x^2$
4. $f(x) = x + 3$ **5.** $f(x) = 2x$ **6.** $f(x) = x + 2$
7. $f(x) = x - 1$ **8.** $f(x) = 3x$ **9.** 15 **10.** 40 **11.** 36
12. 2 **13.** 4 **14.** 9 **15a.** Answers may vary. Sample:
$M(n) = 30n$ **15b.** 180 in. **15c.** 75 in. **16a.** Answers may
vary. Sample: $C(n) = 0.20n$ **16b.** $2.40 **17a.** Answers may
vary. Sample: $P(n) = 9.50n - 209$ **17b.** $19 **17c.** 22 shirts
18a. Answers may vary. Sample: $C(m) = 25 + 0.20m$
18b. $55

Practice 2-5: Mixed Examples
1. $f(x) = x + 3$ **2.** $f(x) = 3x$ **3.** $f(x) = x - 5$
4a. Answers may vary. Sample: $B(p) = 0.39p$ **4b.** $1.37
5a. Answers may vary. Sample: $C(n) = 50 + 10n$
5b. $110 **6.** 4 **7.** 19 **8.** 14 **9.** -12 **10.** 10 **11.** 5
12. $f(x) = \frac{1}{2}x$ **13.** $f(x) = x^2$ **14.** $f(x) = 20 - x$
15. $\{0, 1, 45\}$ **16.** $\{27, 24, 12\}$ **17.** $\{8, 7, 3\}$
18a. Answers may vary. Sample: $N(b) = 12b$ **18b.** 192 pens
19a. Answers may vary. Sample: $C(n) = 20 - 1.25n$
19b. $13.75 **19c.** no

4. Independent variable is number of pencils; dependent
variable is cost of pencils. **5.** Independent variable is cost
of item; dependent variable is change from twenty.
6. Independent variable is speed of car; dependent variable is
distance traveled. **7.** Independent variable is cost of items;
dependent variable is amount of sales tax. **8.** Answers may
vary. Sample: x-values: scale -6 to 14, interval of 2; y-values:
scale -25 to 10, interval of 5 **9.** Answers may vary. Sample: x-
values: scale -20 to 4, interval of 4; y-values: scale -50 to 75,
interval of 25 **10.** Answers may vary. Sample: x-values: scale 0
to 28, interval of 4; y-values: scale 3 to 13, interval of 1.5
11a. As the amount of carpet increases, the total cost increases.
11b. Independent variable is amount of carpet; dependent
variable is total cost.

11c.

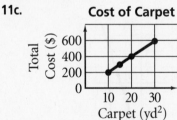

Cost of Carpet

12a. Independent variable is miles driven; dependent variable
is total cost.

12b.

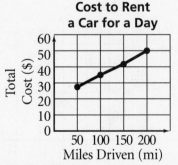

Cost to Rent
a Car for a Day

12c. Answers may vary. Sample: $38 **12d.** As the miles driven
increase the cost to rent the car increases.

Chapter 2 Answers (continued)

Practice 2-6: Example Exercises

For Exercises 1–11 answers may vary. Samples:

1.

x	f(x)
0	−6
2	−4
4	−2
6	0

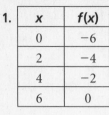

2.

x	f(x)
0	15
6	9
10	5
15	0

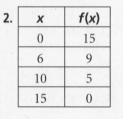

3.

x	f(x)
−1	5
0	0
1	−5
2	−10

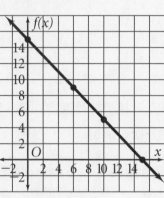

4.

x	f(x)
−2	1
0	2
2	3
4	4

5.

x	f(x)
−3	6
0	4
3	2
6	0

6.

x	f(x)
−1	8
0	5
1	2
2	−1

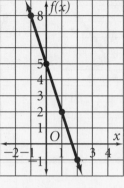

7.

x	f(x)
−1	−5
0	−3
1	−1
2	1

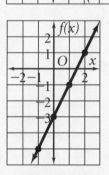

8.

x	f(x)
−2	0
0	−2
1	−3
3	−5

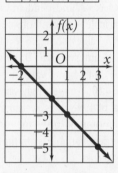

9.

x	f(x)
0	−8
1	−5
2	−2
4	4

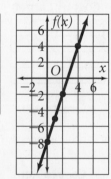

10a.

n	C(n)
1	$50
2	$100
3	$150
4	$200

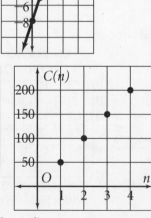

10b. $650   **10c.** No; the data is discrete.

Chapter 2 Answers (continued)

11a.

t	S(t)
1	32
2	64
3	96
4	128

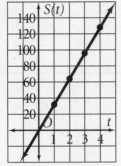

11b. 48 ft/s   **11c.** Yes; the data is continuous.

12.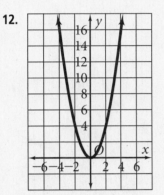

13.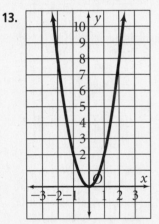

14.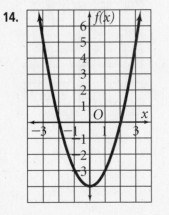

15.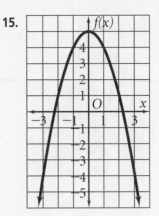

16.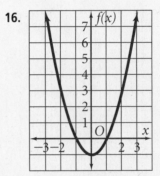

17.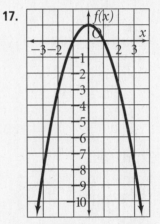

18.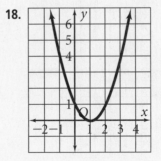

19.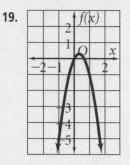

20.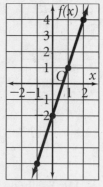

3.

x	f(x)
−1	−5
0	−2
1	1
2	4

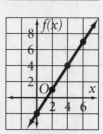

21.

x	y
0	−1
1	0
2	1
3	2

22.

x	y
0	−3
1	−3
3	−3
5	−3

4.

x	f(x)
0	−2
2	1
4	4
6	7

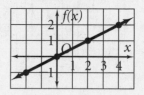

5.

x	f(x)
−2	−1
0	0
2	1
4	2

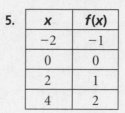

23.

x	y
−1	−1
0	0
1	−1
2	−4

6.

x	f(x)
−3	3
0	1
3	−1
6	−3

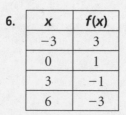

Practice 2-6: Mixed Exercises

For Exercises 1−11 answers may vary. Sample:

1.

x	f(x)
−1	0
0	1
1	2
2	3

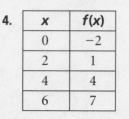

7.

x	f(x)
−1	2
0	1
1	2
2	5

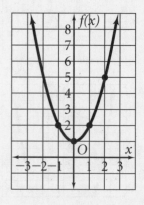

2.

x	f(x)
−2	−4
−1	−2
0	0
1	2

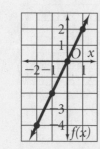

8.

x	f(x)
−2	−2
0	2
2	−2
4	−14

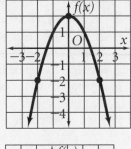

9.

x	f(x)
−3	−6
0	−3
3	0
6	3

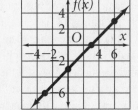

10a.

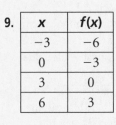

10b. 231 mi   **10c.** Yes; the values are continuous.

11a.

n	T(n)
1	3.50
2	4.00
3	4.50
4	5.00

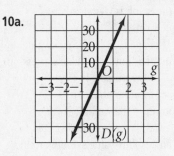

11b. $6.00   **11c.** No; the values are discrete.

12.

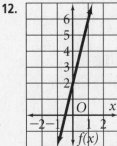

13.

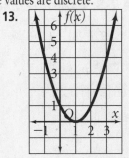

14.

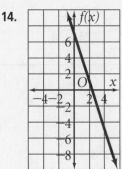

15.

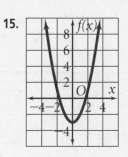

16.

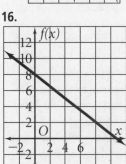

17.

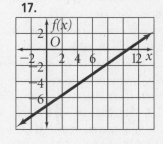

18.

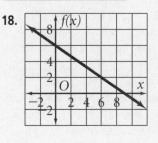

19.

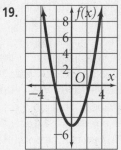

20.

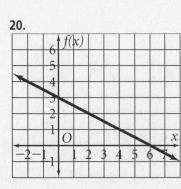

21.

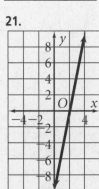

22.

23.

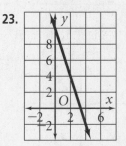

Chapter 2 Answers (continued)

For Exercises 24–26 answers may vary. Sample:

24.

x	y
0	−1
1	1
2	3
3	5

25.

x	y
−1	5
0	2
1	−1
2	−4

26.

x	y
−2	2
−1	0
0	0
1	2

Practice 2-7: Example Exercises

1. The highest power of the variable is 1. **2.** The highest power of the variable is 2. **3.** There is an absolute value symbol around a variable expression. **4.** Linear; the highest power of the variable is 1. **5.** Linear; the highest power of the variable is 1. **6.** Quadratic; the highest power of the variable is 2. **7.** Absolute value; there is an absolute value symbol around a variable expression. **8.** Linear; the highest power of the variable is 1. **9.** Quadratic; the highest power of the variable is 2. **10.** Absolute value; there is an absolute value symbol around a variable expression. **11.** Quadratic; the highest power of the variable is 2. **12.** Answers may vary. Sample: $y = 2x + 5$, $y = -x$ **13.** The absolute value symbol is not around the variable expression. **14.** The graph forms a straight line. **15.** The graph has a U-shaped curve that opens up or down. **16.** The graph forms a "V" that opens up or down. **17.** Absolute value; the graph forms a "V." **18.** Quadratic; the graph is U-shaped. **19.** Quadratic; the graph is U-shaped. **20.** Linear; the graph forms a straight line. **21.** Absolute value; the graph forms a "V." **22.** Linear; the graph forms a straight line. **23.** Answers may vary. Sample:

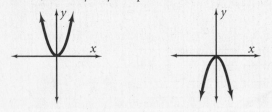

Practice 2-7: Mixed Exercises

1. Answers may vary. Sample: $y = x^2$, $y = 3x^2 + 2$, $y = x^2 + 2x$ **2.** Answers may vary. Sample: $y = |x|$, $y = 2 - |x|$, $y = |x - 3|$

3. Answers may vary. Sample:

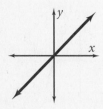

4. Absolute value; there is an absolute value symbol around the variable expression. **5.** Quadratic; the highest power of the variable is 2. **6.** Absolute value; there is an absolute value symbol around the variable expression. **7.** Linear; the highest power of the variable is 1. **8.** Absolute value; there is an absolute value symbol around the variable expression. **9.** Quadratic; the highest power of the variable is 2. **10.** Quadratic; the highest power of the variable is 2. **11.** Linear; the highest power of the variable is 1. **12.** Absolute value; there is an absolute value symbol around the variable expression. **13.** Linear; the highest power of the variable is 1. **14.** Absolute value; there is an absolute value symbol around the variable expression. **15.** Quadratic; the highest power of the variable is 2. **16.** Absolute value; the graph forms a "V." **17.** Linear; the graph forms a straight line. **18.** Quadratic; the graph is U-shaped. **19.** Quadratic; the graph is U-shaped. **20.** Absolute value; the graph forms a "V." **21.** Quadratic; the graph is U-shaped. **22.** Absolute value; there is an absolute value symbol around a variable expression. **23.** Linear; the highest power of the variable is 1. **24.** Linear; the highest power of the variable is 1. **25.** Quadratic; the highest power of the variable is 2. **26.** Quadratic; the highest power of the variable is 2. **27.** Absolute value; there is an absolute value symbol around the variable expression. **28.** Quadratic; the highest power of the variable is 2. **29.** Linear; the highest power of the variable is 1. **30.** Linear; the highest power of the variable is 1. **31.** Absolute value; there is an absolute value symbol around a variable expression. **32.** Linear; the highest power of the variable is 1. **33.** Quadratic; the highest power of the variable is 2. **34.** Quadratic; the highest power of the variable is 2. **35.** Absolute value; there is an absolute value symbol around a variable expression. **36.** Linear; the highest power of the variable is 1.

Practice 2-8: Example Exercises

1. $\frac{1}{6}$ **2.** $\frac{2}{3}$ **3.** 0 **4.** $\frac{1}{50}$ **5.** $\frac{2}{25}$ **6.** $\frac{1}{10}$ **7.** 75%

8. $\frac{1}{4}$ **9a.** $\frac{1}{6}$ **9b.** $\frac{5}{6}$ **9c.** $\frac{7}{12}$ **9d.** $\frac{5}{12}$

10. HHH, HHT, HTH, HTT, THH, THT, TTH, TTT

11a. $\frac{3}{8}$ **11b.** $\frac{1}{2}$ **11c.** $\frac{3}{8}$

12. 222, 225, 227, 252, 255, 257, 272, 275, 277, 522, 525, 527, 552, 555, 557, 572, 575, 577, 722, 725, 727, 752, 755, 757, 772, 775, 777

13a. $\frac{1}{27}$ **13b.** $\frac{19}{27}$ **13c.** $\frac{12}{27}$

14a. 0 **14b.** $\frac{2}{3}$ **14c.** $\frac{1}{6}$ **14d.** $\frac{1}{2}$

Practice 2-8: Mixed Exercises

1a. $\frac{2}{7}$ **1b.** $\frac{3}{7}$ **1c.** $\frac{3}{7}$ **2.** 60%

3a. RRR, RRB, RBR, RBB, BRR, BRB, BBR, BBB **3b.** $\frac{1}{2}$

3c. $\frac{3}{4}$ **3d.** $\frac{1}{4}$ **4a.** $\frac{5}{14}$ **4b.** $\frac{5}{7}$ **4c.** $\frac{3}{7}$

5a. $\frac{4}{13}$ **5b.** $\frac{8}{13}$ **5c.** $\frac{7}{13}$

6a. $\frac{1}{6}$ **6b.** $\frac{1}{2}$ **6c.** $\frac{5}{6}$ **7.** $\frac{25}{26}$

8a. AB, AC, AD, BC, BD, CD **8b.** $\frac{1}{6}$ **8c.** $\frac{1}{2}$ **8d.** $\frac{1}{3}$

9a. $\frac{4}{11}$ **9b.** $\frac{5}{11}$ **9c.** $\frac{6}{11}$

✔ Checkpoint 1: For use after 2-2

1a.–b.

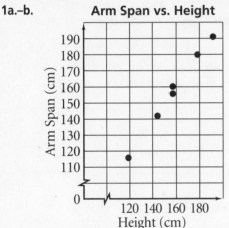

Arm Span vs. Height

1c. Positive correlation.
2. Answers may vary. Sample: If you have a twenty-dollar bill, the more money you spend, the less money you have left.
3. C; this is the only graph that does not end up with a total distance of zero.

✔ Checkpoint 2: For use after 2-5

1a. Independent variable is number of hours. Dependent variable is number of miles.

1b.

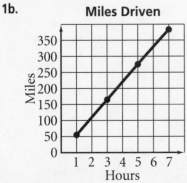

Miles Driven

2. Continuous data usually involves measurements like temperatures, lengths, and weights. Discrete data involves a count, like numbers of people or objects.

3. Answers may vary. Sample: $\{(1, 2), (1, 3), (1, 4)\}$. **4.** $d = 3t$
5. $m = 5.5c$ **6.** $\{-6, 0, 9, 18\}$ **7.** $\{2, -6, -3, 18\}$ **8.** $\{-2.5, 1.5, 7.5, 13.5\}$ **9.** $\{6, 14, 11, -10\}$

Chapter Assessment, Form A

1. negative correlation **2.** no correlation **3.** positive correlation **4.** Graph 1
5.

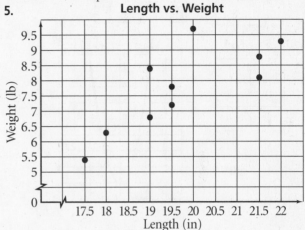

Length vs. Weight

6. Answers may vary. Sample: Length 17 to 23 by 0.5; Weight 4.5 to 10 by 0.5 **7.** continuous **8.** discrete
9. Answers may vary. Sample:

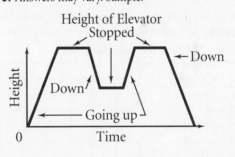

10. Answers may vary. Sample:

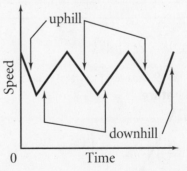

11. yes **12.** no **13.** yes **14.** no **15.** $\{14, 8, 6, 3, -4\}$
16. $\{44, -1, -4, 2.75, 71\}$ **17.** $\{20, 0, 3.75, 30\}$
18. $C(n) = 35n$; cost is the dependent variable; number of nights is the independent variable. **19.** $M(n) = 5.5n$; amount is the dependent variable; number of hours is the independent variable. **20.** $C(p) = 5 - 0.89p$; amount of change is the dependent variable, number of pounds is the independent variable.

21–23. Answers may vary. Sample:

21.

x	f(x)
−2	−1
0	2
2	5
4	8

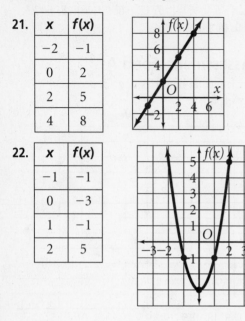

23.

x	f(x)
−1	6
0	4
1	2
2	0

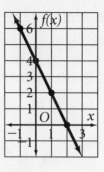

22.

x	f(x)
−1	−1
0	−3
1	−1
2	5

24. A relation is a function when each value in the domain goes to one value in the range. **25.** Answers may vary. Sample: change from a ten-dollar bill. **26.** A

27a. (Chevrolet, compact), (Chevrolet, midsize), (Chevrolet, full-size), (Ford, compact), (Ford, midsize), (Ford, full-size), (Toyota, compact), (Toyota, midsize), (Toyota, full-size), (Honda, compact), (Honda, midsize), (Honda, full-size)

27b. $\frac{1}{12}$ **28.** C **29.** If you can draw a vertical line that passes through more than one point, then the graph is not a function graph. Otherwise it is a function graph.

Chapter Assessment, Form B

1. positive correlation **2.** negative correlation **3.** no correlation **4.** Graph 3
5. Answers may vary. Sample: Waist 28 to 39 by 1; shoe size 7 to 12 by 0.5
6.

Shoe Size vs. Waist Size

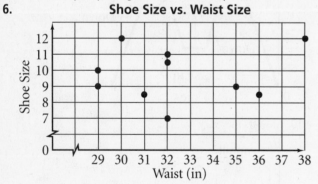

7. discrete **8.** continuous **9.** Answers may vary. Sample:

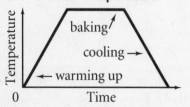

10. no **11.** yes **12.** no **13.** yes **14.** {−1, −4, −7, −145, −25} **15.** {12, 6, 4, 16.5, 76} **16.** $f(g) = \{−1.5, 0.5, 2.5, 7.5, 14.5\}$
17. $D(t) = 250t$; distance is the dependent variable; time is the independent variable. **18.** $C(g) = 20 − 1.15g$; change is the dependent variable; gallons is the independent variable.

© Prentice-Hall, Inc.

Chapter 2 Answers (continued)

19–21. Answers may vary. Samples:

19.

x	f(x)
−2	2
0	−2
2	2
4	14

20.

x	f(x)
−3	6
0	4
3	2
6	0

21.

x	f(x)
−2	−2
0	2
1	1
2	−2

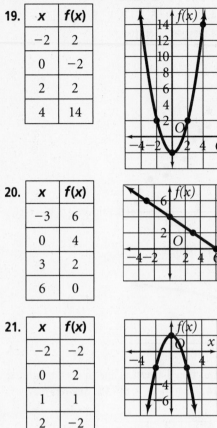

22. A relation and a function are the same because they are both sets of ordered pairs. They are different because a function is a special type of relation when each value in the domain goes to one value in the range. **23.** Answers may vary. Sample: the cost of notebooks at $2 each **24.** C

25a. (small, short, white), (small, short, blue), (small, long, white), (small, long, blue), (medium, short, white), (medium, short, blue), (medium, long, white), (medium, long, blue), (large, short, white), (large, short, blue), (large, long, white), (large, long, blue) **25b.** $\frac{1}{12}$ **26.** C **27a.** function

27b. not a function **27c.** not a function **27d.** function

Alternative Assessment

TASK 1 Scoring Guide:

a.

b. positive

3 Scatter plot is accurately drawn with no errors. Explanation of correlation is thorough and clearly demonstrates an understanding of the underlying mathematical principals.
2 Scatter plot is correctly drawn, with only minor errors in scale and accuracy. Explanation of correlation is well stated.
1 Scale and accuracy of scatter plot are partially correct. Correlation may be incorrect.
0 The student makes no attempt or no solution is presented.

TASK 2 Scoring Guide:

3 Student writes a story and makes a sketch that shows significant understanding of the relationship between time and distance. Variables relate to the story and are used correctly.
2 The sketch is mostly correct, but contains minor errors related to the story or the variables.
1 The response is partially satisfactory, but there are major errors.
0 The student makes no attempt or no solution is presented.

TASK 3 Scoring Guide:

d. 16; the dependent variable is y and the independent variable is x.
3 Student writes explanations that show an in-depth understanding of the relevant mathematical ideas and processes. Examples presented are appropriate and clearly support the student's definition. Function rule is correct based on table of values.
2 Definition and explanations are essentially correct but could be more thorough. Graphs are mostly correct. Function rule relates to table of values.
1 Definition and explanations are sketchy. Examples or function rule are incorrect.
0 The student makes no attempt or no solution is present.

Chapter 2 Answers (continued)

TASK 4 Scoring Guide:

a. $\frac{2}{9}$; $\frac{5}{18}$; $\frac{13}{18}$; $\frac{1}{3}$ **b.** white **c.** Answers may vary. Sample: selecting the keys to an orange car. **d.** BBB, BBG, BGB, BGG, GBB, GBG, GGB, GGG; $\frac{3}{8}$

3 Student demonstrates understanding of probability. Answers given are correct and reasonable. Tree diagram is accurate and clearly demonstrates understanding of the underlying mathematical principals.

2 Understanding of probability is essentially sound but could be more accurate. Answers are mostly correct. Tree diagram is essentially accurate, but incomplete.

1 Understanding is limited with obvious inaccuracies. Tree diagram is incomplete or incorrect.

0 Student makes no attempt or no solution is presented.

Cumulative Review

1. B **2.** C **3.** D **4.** B **5.** A **6.** C **7.** D **8.** A

9. $\{33, 7, 0, -2\}$ **10a.** linear; the highest power of the variable is 1. **10b.** quadratic; the highest power of the variable is 2. **10c.** quadratic; the highest power of the variable is 2. **10d.** absolute value; there is an absolute value symbol around the variable expression. **11.** Continuous data usually involves measurements like temperatures, lengths, and weights. Discrete data involves a count, like numbers of people or objects. **12.** Answers may vary. Sample: The cost of buying four items.

13a. $\frac{2}{13}$ **13b.** $\frac{11}{13}$ **13c.** $\frac{7}{13}$

14a. $\frac{5}{36}$ **14b.** $\frac{1}{6}$ **14c.** $\frac{1}{2}$

15a. The independent variable is time and the dependent variable is distance.

15b.

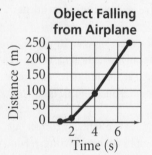

Object Falling from Airplane

15c. Answers may vary. Sample: 120 m

Standardized Test Practice

1. A **2.** C **3.** D **4.** A **5.** B **6.** C **7.** B **8.** E **9.** D **10.** C **11.** Answers may vary. Sample:

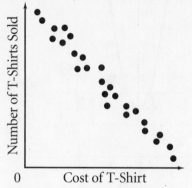

12. Answers may vary. Sample:

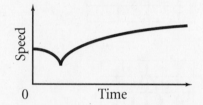

13. The graph is a function if a vertical line passes through the graph only once. **14.** range = $\{5, 7, 8\}$ **15.** Answers may vary. Sample:

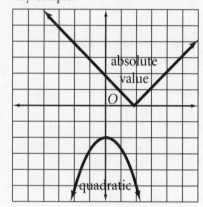

16. $\frac{5}{26}$ **17.** -2 **18.** 2